WEST HAM UNITED

QUIZ BOOK 2

Published by twocan

©2019. Published by twocan under licence from West Ham United FC.

ISBN: 978-1-912692-91-0

PICTURE CREDITS: Getty Images

COMPILED BY PETER ROGERS

INTRODUCTION

Having made my first visit to the Boleyn Ground back in the late 1980s, I soon realised that the West Ham supporters were a passionate and knowledgeable crowd who had a real appetite for quality passing football.

This latest collection of 100 quizzes has been set to focus and reflect the club's fortunes in the Premier League era. Complied to feature a range of questions - there will be some that all supporters will know the answer to, a selection that will put your Hammers' knowledge to the test and also a few that will even get the real bubbles brain-boxes scratching their heads for the answer.

There are quizzes covering each of the club's Premier League campaigns and there is also a quiz relating to all of the opposing teams that the Hammers have faced at Premier League level, plus a set of questions on all of the club's permanent Premier League managers.

So from goalscorers to goalkeepers and line-ups to loan signings, it's time get those claret and blue brains fully in gear. With 1000 questions to tackle there is something for all fans regardless of how long you've been following the Hammers' fortunes fluctuate.

See how many of the questions you can get right - there are a number of questions with a simple true or false answer and also a number of questions with multiple choice answers. Hopefully there will be something over the coming pages for everyone and this book may well help pass the miles en route to away matches when perhaps a little bit of friendly in-car or on-coach competition can take place.

I would also like to acknowledge many sources including the Rothmans/ Sky Sports Football Yearbooks, whufc.com, soccerbase.com and finally westhamstats.info which is an impressive online collection of facts, figures and memorabilia relating to the wonderful world of West Ham United.

Come On You Irons!

PETER ROGERS

THE PREMIER LEAGUE

1. In which season was the Premier League formed?

2. How many teams make up the current Premier League?

3. Ahead of the 2019/20 season how many different clubs have won the Premier League title?

4. In which season did the Hammers first compete in the Premier League?

5. At the end of the 2019/20 campaign, how many seasons will West Ham have competed in the Premier League?

6. Who are the only company to have been title sponsors of the Premier League?

7. How many different clubs have the Hammers played at Premier League level - 44, 46 or 48?

8. How many men have managed West Ham in the Premier League?

9. Who has made the most Premier League appearances for the Hammers?

10. How many clubs based outside of England have the Hammers faced in Premier League fixtures?

THE 1993/94 SEASON

11. Who was West Ham manager when they began their maiden Premier League campaign?

12. Which club provided the Hammers' first Premier League opposition?

13. At which venue did West Ham's first Premier League fixture take place?

14. Who scored the club's first Premier League goal?

15. Against which side did the Hammers record their first Premier League victory?

16. On which away ground did West Ham win their first Premier League away fixture?

17. Who ended the 1993/94 season as the Hammers' leading scorer with 13 Premier League goals?

18. Which club won the Premier League title in 1993/94?

19. Against which club did the Hammers conclude their first Premier League campaign with a final day 3-3 draw?

20. What was West Ham's final league position in 1993/94?

ARSENAL

21. Who was the West Ham 'keeper who recorded a clean sheet when the Hammers first played the Gunners in the Premier League?

22. Can you name the first West Ham player to score a Premier League goal against Arsenal?

23. Billy Bonds was West Ham manager when they first faced Arsenal in the Premier League - true or false?

24. In which season did the clubs face one another in the Premier League, the League Cup and the FA Cup?

25. Can you recall the season that West Ham first recorded a Premier League double over Arsenal?

26. What was the score when the Hammers last played Arsenal in a Premier League match at Highbury?

27. Can you name the striker that the Hammers signed from Premier League rivals Arsenal in February 1997?

28. Who was the Hammers' hat-trick hero in a 3-3 Premier League draw with Arsenal in April 2016?

29. In which season did the Hammers first defeat Arsenal at London Stadium?

30. West Ham began their 2019/20 Premier League campaign by hosting Arsenal - true or false?

ASTON VILLA

31. Aston Villa's 2019/20 Premier League match with the Hammers will be Villa's first visit to London Stadium - true or false?

32. Who was the first Hammer to score a winning goal against Villa at Premier League level?

33. Ahead of the 2019/20 season, when did the Hammers last double Aston Villa in the Premier League?

34. Can you name the West Ham striker who netted a hat-trick against Villa in the Hammers' 4-0 victory at the Boleyn Ground in September 2005?

35. Who scored the Hammers' last goal against Villa at the Boleyn Ground?

36. What was the score when the two sides met at Villa Park on Boxing Day 2015?

37. Who netted a brace for the Hammers in the 2-1 home win over Villa in November 1997?

38. Sam Allardyce has managed both clubs at Premier League level - true or false?

39. Who scored the Hammers' final goal of the 2007/08 season to salvage a point in a final day 2-2 draw with Villa?

40. Can you name the Welsh international defender who has played in the Premier League for both clubs?

41. In which season did the Hammers first face Barnsley in the Premier League?

42. The two clubs have only met as Premier League opponents in one season - true or false?

43. At which ground was the Hammers' first Premier League fixture against Barnsley played?

44. Who was West Ham manager when the club first faced the Tykes in the Premier League?

45. West Ham came from behind to win their first Premier League match against Barnsley. Who opened the scoring for the Tykes before the Hammers won 2-1?

46. Can you name the two West Ham players who scored in both games against the Tykes in the first season they met in the Premier League?

47. West Ham ran out comfortable 6-0 winners in their second Premier League meeting with Barnsley. How many different players scored in that game?

48. Can you recall the Hammer who netted a brace in the above fixture?

49. Who was the Hammers 'keeper in that 6-0 victory?

50. Although the Hammers and Tykes have met in the Premier League, they never faced one another in the old First Division - true or false?

QUIZ 6
BIRMINGHAM CITY

51. In which season did West Ham first play Birmingham at Premier League level?

52. Who was the first Hammer to score a Premier League goal against Blues?

53. Can you recall who managed West Ham for their first Premier League match at St Andrew's?

54. In December 2005, who became the first West Ham player to score a winning Premier League goal against Birmingham City?

55. In which season did West Ham first complete a Premier League double over Birmingham?

56. Can you name the Hammers' scorer from their 1-0 win away to Blues in August 2007?

57. Which West Ham midfielder saw red in the closing stages of a 1-1 draw between the two sides at the Boleyn Ground in February 2008?

58. Alan Curbishley, who managed the Hammers in the Premier League, played for Birmingham City earlier in his career - true or false?

59. In 2010/11 the Hammers faced Birmingham in the Premier League and also in which cup competition?

60. In which season did the two clubs last meet in the Premier League?

CAPTAIN CALLING

Long-serving defender Steve Potts captained the Hammers to an eventful 3-3 draw with Southampton in the final game of their 1993/94 Premier League campaign - can you name his ten teammates that started the match? (4-5-1 with Potts in central defence)

61.   Goalkeeper? (five letters & eight letters)

62.   Right-back? (three letters & eight letters)

63.   Left-back? (five letters & seven letters)

64.   Central defender? (four letters & four letters)

65.   Midfielder? (six letters & five letters)

66.   Midfielder? (three letters & six letters)

67.   Midfielder? (four letters & five letters)

68.   Midfielder? (seven letters & four letters)

69.   Midfielder? (five letters & ten letters)

70.   Striker? (six letters & six letters)

71. Can you name the Hammers' two ever-present players from the 1994/95 Premier League campaign?

72. How many games into the season was it until the Hammers won their first Premier League fixture?

73. Against which club did the Hammers record their first league win of the season?

74. Who scored the club's first league goal of the season in a 3-1 home defeat to Newcastle United?

75. Which Hammer netted the first winning goal of the 1994/95 campaign?

76. On Boxing Day 1994 the Hammers welcomed which East Anglian club to the Boleyn Ground - Norwich City or Ipswich Town?

77. Who was the club's leading Premier League scorer in 1994/95?

78. Can you name the player who scored the Hammers' final goal of the season in a 1-1 draw at home to Manchester United?

79. Who was voted Hammer of the Year at the end of the 1994/95 season?

80. In which position in the Premier League table did the Hammers finish in 1994/95?

BLACKBURN ROVERS

81. When Blackburn Rovers won the title in 1994/95 what were the two scorelines from their fixtures against the Hammers?

82. In which season did the Hammers first play a Premier League game against Blackburn?

83. Rovers' striker Alan Shearer netted consecutive hat-tricks against West Ham at Ewood Park in 1994/95 and 1995/96 - true or false?

84. Who has managed both the Hammers and Rovers in the Premier League?

85. Can you name the Hammers' goalkeeper who conceded seven goals in a Premier League match away to Blackburn in October 2001?

86. In which season did West Ham record their first Premier League double over Blackburn Rovers?

87. Who scored the only goal of the game to give West Ham a 1-0 win at Ewood Park in December 2007?

88. Which West Ham youngster marked his first-team debut with a goal to seal a 2-1 win over Blackburn at the Boleyn Ground in March 2008?

89. Which Australian international defender joined West Ham from Blackburn in 2007?

90. Who was the last West Ham player to score a Premier League goal against Blackburn Rovers?

BLACKPOOL

91. West Ham and Blackpool have only met as Premier League opponents in one season but can you recall which season?

92. Can you name the Blackpool boss for their two Premier League fixtures against the Hammers?

93. Who was the Hammers' manager when they faced Blackpool in the Premier League?

94. Which venue hosted the first ever Premier League meeting between the two clubs - the Boleyn Ground or Bloomfield Road?

95. The first Premier League match between the two clubs ended goalless. Can you name the two goalkeepers who registered clean sheets that day?

96. Which former West Ham striker played for Blackpool in both their Premier League games against the Hammers?

97. Can you name the Hammers' striker who netted a brace in the 3-1 victory over Blackpool in the second meeting of the season?

98. Which loan signing marked his West Ham debut with a Premier League goal against Blackpool?

99. After facing one another in the Premier League for the first time, both clubs were relegated at the end of the season, but who went down with them?

100. The following season West Ham and Blackpool went head-to-head for a place back in the Premier League when they met in the Championship Play-Off final - true or false?

HAMMER OF THE YEAR

101. Who was the first West Ham player to land the Hammer of the Year award in the Premier League?

102. Which player was the first to be voted Hammer of the Year on a back-to-back basis in the Premier League era?

103. Can you name the first goalkeeper to win the award following a Premier League campaign?

104. In 2001/02 who received the Hammer of the Year accolade?

105. Which home-grown player was Hammer of the Year runner-up in 2001/02 but won the award the following season?

106. When Carlos Tevez won the award in 2006/07, how many Premier League goals did he score - seven, nine or eleven?

107. Can you name the former England left-back who won the award in 2000/01?

108. Who won the award prior to Scott Parker's hat-trick of titles?

109. In which season did Scott Parker win the first of his three consecutive Hammer of the Year awards?

110. Which former youth team star won the Hammer of the Year award in 1997/98 - Frank Lampard (Jnr), Joe Cole or Rio Ferdinand?

QUIZ 12
HARRY REDKNAPP

111. At the start of which Premier League campaign was Harry appointed West Ham manager?

112. Which young midfielder did Redknapp hand a Premier League debut to in an away match at Bradford City in August 1999?

113. In January 1998 Redknapp signed Trevor Sinclair from which club?

114. Can you name the two West Ham players that Redknapp sent in the opposite direction to form part of the deal to sign Sinclair?

115. After starring for Romania in Euro96 can you name the striker Redknapp signed from Espanyol for the 1996/97 Premier League campaign?

116. What was the highest Premier League finish that the Hammers managed under Harry Redknapp?

117. In which season was that best Premier League finish achieved?

118. Which former West Ham favourite assisted Redknapp during his spell as West Ham boss?

119. Against which club did the Hammers record a 3-0 win at the Boleyn Ground in his final game in charge?

120. Who succeeded Redknapp as West Ham manager ahead of the club's 2001/02 Premier League campaign?

QUIZ 13
BOLTON WANDERERS

121. Glenn Roeder has managed both West Ham and Bolton in Premier League fixtures - true or false?

122. In the 2009/10 campaign, West Ham and Bolton faced one another in the Premier League and in which domestic cup competition?

123. Whose 89th-minute goal in May 2002 secured West Ham a 2-1 final day victory over Bolton Wanderers at the Boleyn Ground?

124. In which season did the Hammers first play Bolton in the Premier League?

125. West Ham recorded a Premier League double over Bolton in the first season they faced one another - true or false?

126. Who was the first West Ham manager to oversee a Premier League victory over Bolton Wanderers?

127. Can you name the West Ham striker who netted a brace in a 3-0 home win over Bolton in October 1997?

128. Who was the first player to score a Premier League goal for West Ham against Bolton - Tony Cottee, Ian Bishop or Danny Williamson?

129. Kevin Nolan played Premier League football for both West Ham and Bolton, but which other Premier League club has he represented?

130. How many times did the Hammers face Bolton in the 2005/06 season?

BOURNEMOUTH

131. When West Ham played Bournemouth in the 2015/16 season this was the first time the two clubs had ever met as league opposition - true or false?

132. Which former England international striker has scored Premier League goals for both the Hammers and Cherries?

133. Who was the Hammers' boss when they first played Bournemouth in the Premier League?

134. Can you name the Bournemouth striker who netted a hat-trick in the first Premier League meeting between the two teams?

135. Who was the first West Ham player to score a Premier League goal against the Cherries?

136. Bournemouth provided the Hammers' final Premier League opposition at the Boleyn Ground - true or false?

137. Who scored a superb free-kick to equalise for the Hammers in the 3-1 win away to Bournemouth in January 2016?

138. What was the score when West Ham defeated Bournemouth in the opening Premier League game at London Stadium?

139. Who opened the scoring for West Ham on Boxing Day 2017 in a thrilling 3-3 draw with Bournemouth at Dean Court?

140. Ahead of the 2019/20 campaign, West Ham have yet to complete a Premier League double over the Cherries - true or false?

BRADFORD CITY

141. The Hammers' 1999/2000 Premier League fixtures with Bradford City were the first time the two clubs had met in the top flight - true or false?

142. Who netted West Ham's opening goal in the 3-0 win away to Bradford in August 1999?

143. West Ham were the first club to inflict a Premier League defeat on the Bantams at Valley Parade - true or false?

144. The Hammers and Bantams served up a nine-goal thriller when West Ham won an epic Premier League match 5-4 in February 2000. How many different players scored in that match?

145. When the two sides drew 1-1 at the Boleyn Ground in September 2000, who opened the scoring for the Hammers?

146. Can you name the Romanian international who rescued a point for Bradford with a 90th-minute equaliser in the above match?

147. Who was the Hammers' two-goal hero when they won 2-1 at Valley Parade in February 2001?

148. Can you name the future West Ham coach who was among the Bradford substitutes in the Premier League meeting in February 2001?

149. Who managed Bradford City for their first Premier League visit to the Boleyn Ground?

150. In which season did the two clubs last meet in the Premier League?

THE 1995/96 SEASON

151. Who netted the Hammers' first goal of the season
in a 2-1 defeat at home to Leeds United?

152. Can you name the Dutch forward who made his debut
in the opening day match with Leeds at the Boleyn Ground?

153. The Hammers made a slow start to the season.
Their first Premier League win came after how
many games - five, six or seven?

154. West Ham's first Premier League away win in 1995/96
came in a London derby against which club?

155. The club's highest home attendance of the season
was 24,324 but who were the opposition - Liverpool,
Arsenal or Manchester United?

156. The Hammers completed a Premier League double
over London rivals Chelsea in 1995/96 - true or false?

157. Which two players ended the season as the club's
joint top league scorers?

158. The 1995/96 season saw Frank Lampard (Jnr) make
his West Ham debut. Against which club did he make
his Premier League bow?

159. Which full-back made his final appearance for
the club in the 1-0 home win over Nottingham Forest
in February 1996?

160. Which central defender made his West Ham debut in the
final game of the season at home to Sheffield Wednesday?

CAPTAIN CALLING

Midfielder Steve Lomas skippered West Ham to a fifth place Premier League finish in 1998/99. The Hammers began the season with a 1-0 win away to Sheffield Wednesday. Can you name Lomas' teammates who got the season off to a winning start? (3-5-2 with Lomas in central midfield)

161. Goalkeeper? (five letters & six letters)

162. Defender? (three letters & six letters)

163. Defender? (three letters & nine letters)

164. Defender? (four letters & seven letters)

165. Right wing-back? (four letters & five letters)

166. Midfielder? (five letters & seven letters)

167. Midfielder? (four letters & eight letters)

168. Left wing-back? (four letters & nine letters)

169. Striker? (six letters & eight letters)

170. Striker? (three letters & six letters)

BRIGHTON & HOVE ALBION

171. Can you name the former West Ham player who managed Brighton to a Premier League victory over the Hammers in October 2017?

172. In which season did the two clubs first face one another as Premier League opponents?

173. Who scored the Hammers' first Premier League goal against Brighton?

174. Can you recall who managed West Ham in their first Premier League match against the Seagulls?

175. Brighton striker Glenn Murray netted four goals in his first four Premier League games for Brighton against West Ham - true or false?

176. Who bagged a second-half brace to secure the Hammers a share of the spoils in a 2-2 draw at the Amex Stadium in January 2019?

177. Current Brighton head coach Graham Potter scored his only Premier League goal for Southampton in a match against West Ham - true or false?

178. Other than in the Premier League, in which other competition have West Ham played Brighton at the Amex Stadium?

179. Ahead of the 2019/20 campaign, the Hammers have yet to keep a Premier League clean sheet against Brighton - true or false?

180. At which venue did the first 2019/20 Premier League meeting between the two clubs take place - London Stadium or the Amex Stadium?

OPENING DAY FIXTURES

181. Who was the Hammers' marksman in their 1998/99 1-0 opening day victory at Sheffield Wednesday?

182. Against which London rivals did the Hammers secure a 1-0 opening day triumph at the Boleyn Ground in 1999/2000?

183. Following a two-season absence from the top flight, who scored the Hammers' first goal in their 3-1 opening day victory over Blackburn Rovers in 2005/06?

184. Who were the opposition when West Ham won an opening day London derby 3-1 in 2006/07?

185. Can you recall which player netted an opening day brace in that 2006/07 victory?

186. Back in the Premier League in 2012/13, who were the Hammers' opening day opponents?

187. Who opened the scoring to give West Ham a memorable 2-0 opening day victory away to Arsenal in 2015/16?

188. Can you name the young midfielder who made his Premier League debut in that 2015 triumph at the Emirates Stadium?

189. Which former West Ham striker lined-up against the Hammers on the opening day of the 2013/14 campaign?

190. Manuel Pellegrini began his reign as West Ham boss in 2018/19 with a tough fixture away to which club?

BURNLEY

191. Who managed West Ham to an eventful 5-3 Premier League victory over Burnley in November 2009?

192. In that 5-3 win West Ham scored two penalties by two different players - can you name them both?

193. Can you name the Brazilian forward who scored the Hammers' consolation goal on his debut in a 2-1 defeat at Turf Moor in February 2010?

194. In which season did West Ham record their first Premier League double over Burnley?

195. Can you name the England international goalkeeper who has played Premier League football for both the Hammers and the Clarets?

196. Who scored the only goal of the game to give West Ham a narrow 1-0 home win over Burnley in the final season at the Boleyn Ground?

197. Andre Ayew scored the Hammers' winning goal away to Burnley in May 2017 - what nationality is Ayew?

198. Which West Ham forward scored twice in the 4-2 triumph over Burnley at London Stadium in 2018/19?

199. Prior to the 2019/20 campaign West Ham have played Burnley in five different Premier League seasons - in which season did the Clarets finish above the Hammers?

200. Can you name the West Ham 'keeper who kept a clean sheet in a 1-0 win at home to Burnley in December 2016?

CARDIFF CITY

201. In which Premier League season did the Hammers first play Cardiff City?

202. Which former West Ham player managed the Bluebirds in an opening day trip to the Boleyn Ground?

203. Can you name the World Cup final referee that took charge of the first Premier League meeting between the Hammers and Cardiff City?

204. Who was the first West Ham player to score a Premier League goal against the Bluebirds?

205. In the first season that the two clubs met in the Premier League, they were also drawn to face one another in the League Cup - true or false?

206. Who was the first West Ham goalkeeper to keep a clean sheet against Cardiff City at Premier League level?

207. Which Hammers' defender was sent off in the 2-0 win away to Cardiff City in January 2014?

208. The Hammers have never played a Premier League match at Ninian Park - true or false?

209. Who scored twice for the Hammers in their 3-1 London Stadium victory over Cardiff City in 2018/19?

210. The Bluebirds were relegated from the Premier League in 2018/19 but which two other clubs went down with them?

CHARLTON ATHLETIC

211. Which two men have managed both West Ham and Charlton at Premier League level?

212. Who was the Hammers' hat-trick hero in the 4-4 Premier League draw away to Charlton in November 2001?

213. Current Charlton boss Lee Bowyer played Premier League Football for West Ham - true or false?

214. Other than West Ham and Charlton can you name the other four clubs that Scott Parker has played for in the Premier League?

215. In which season did the Hammers first play Charlton in the Premier League?

216. Can you recall the last season that the Hammers faced Charlton in the Premier League?

217. How many games have the Hammers won against Charlton in Premier League - three, five or seven?

218. Who opened the scoring from the penalty spot for the Hammers in a 2-0 home win over Charlton in April 2002?

219. Can you name the Hammers' goalkeeper who kept a clean sheet in the above game?

220. Which long-serving Charlton defender scored an own goal to put West Ham in front in the first Premier League meeting between the two clubs ?

221. Chelsea have provided opposition in all of the Hammers' Premier League campaigns - true or false?

222. What was the reported transfer fee when Frank Lampard (Jnr) left West Ham for Chelsea in June 2001?

223. Who scored the only goal of the game to give West Ham a 1-0 victory in the first Premier League match between the two clubs in October 1993?

224. Can you name the Senegalese striker who has played in the Premier League for both West Ham and Chelsea?

225. In which season did the Hammers' two Premier League fixtures against Chelsea both fail to produce a goal?

226. Which Chelsea legend became West Ham manager in 2008?

227. In which season did the Hammers complete their first Premier League double over Chelsea?

228. Who began a second spell with West Ham when he joined the club on loan from Chelsea in August 2012?

229. In what minute of the game did Marko Arnautovic score to give West Ham a 1-0 home win over Chelsea in 2017/18 - sixth minute, 16th minute or 26th minute?

230. Which future England right-back left West Ham for Chelsea in the summer of 2003?

COVENTRY CITY

231. Which two Wales international strikers have played in the Premier League for both West Ham and Coventry City?

232. West Ham secured their first ever Premier League point with a 1-1 draw against Coventry City - true or false?

233. At which venue did the Hammers' first Premier League match with the Sky Blues take place?

234. Can you name the Northern Ireland international who played for West Ham in the Premier League and later managed Coventry City?

235. Who was the West Ham goalkeeper who kept a clean sheet in the Hammers' final Premier League match at Highfield Road in September 2000?

236. Which West Ham player opened the scoring in a 5-0 rout of the Sky Blues at the Boleyn Ground in the 1999/2000 season - Paulo Di Canio, Trevor Sinclair or Michael Carrick?

237. David Burrows played in the Premier League for both West Ham and Coventry City - but which of the two clubs did he play for first?

238. Which two West Ham players scored in both Premier League matches against the Sky Blues in the 1995/96 season?

239. February 2001 saw the Hammers' last Premier League match against Coventry City end 1-1 - can you recall the West Ham goalscorer?

240. Which West Ham defender scored a 90th-minute own goal to ensure honours ended even in that last Premier League meeting?

THE 1996/97 SEASON

241. Which Portuguese international joined the Hammers on a one-year deal ahead of their 1996/97 Premier League campaign?

242. Paul Kitson ended the season as West Ham's leading Premier League scorer, who many goals did he score - eight, nine or ten?

243. Can you name the future Hammer who opened the scoring for Spurs against West Ham in February 1997?

244. Who scored twice for the Hammers in the above mentioned London derby with Spurs?

245. A classic Premier League London derby - what was the final score in the home match with Spurs in February 1997?

246. Who scored the Hammers' first Premier League Goal of the Season?

247. Goalkeeper Ludek Miklosko was the club's top Premier League appearance maker with 38 outings in 1996/97 - what nationality is Miklosko?

248. Can you name the two 'keepers that featured in the two Premier League games that Miklosko missed in 1996/97?

249. The lowest attendance for a Premier League match at the Boleyn Ground in 1996/97 was 19,105. Who were the opposition - Aston Villa, Blackburn Rovers or Derby County?

250. Julian Dicks was voted Hammer of the Year at the end of the 1996/97 season but who was runner-up?

BOXING DAY FIXTURES

251. Who scored twice for the Hammers in their 3-3 draw at Bournemouth on Boxing Day 2017?

252. West Ham's first Premier League Boxing Day goal came in 1994 - can you name the player who scored it?

253. Against which club did the Hammers run out 4-1 away winners on Boxing Day 2016?

254. Who opened the scoring for West Ham in their London derby match with Arsenal on Boxing Day 2013?

255. With which Midlands club did the Hammers play out a 1-1 draw on Boxing Day 2011?

256. West Ham's 1-0 win over Coventry City on Boxing Day 1997 saw them complete a Premier League double over the Sky Blues - true or false?

257. On Boxing Day 2006, the Hammers suffered a 2-1 defeat at home to which Premier League rival - Portsmouth, Reading or Watford?

258. Can you name the Peruvian international who was on target in the Hammers' 2007 Boxing Day match with Reading?

259. Who grabbed a second-half brace in the Hammers' 4-1 Premier League win away to Portsmouth on Boxing Day 2008?

260. Can you name the West Ham goalkeeper who kept a Boxing Day clean sheet against Portsmouth in 2009?

CRYSTAL PALACE

261. Who scored the only goal of the game to give West Ham a win over the Eagles in their first Premier League meeting in October 1994?

262. The Hammers completed a Premier League double over Palace in 1994/95 - true or false?

263. In which season did the Hammers record their first Premier League double over the Eagles?

264. Can you recall the Premier League campaign that saw the Hammers and the Eagles secure 3-1 away wins against one another?

265. Who converted the Hammers' first-half penalty in a 1-1 draw at Selhurst Park in February 2019?

266. Can you name the Hammers' goalscorer in their 1-0 win away to the Eagles in October 2016?

267. Which West Ham defender was sent off in the above match?

268. Who left West Ham in the summer of 2016 to join Crystal Place in a £10M deal?

269. Senegalese international Cheikou Kouyate has played Premier League Football for both the Hammers and the Eagles - true or false?

270. Can you name the Wales international defender who has played in the Premier League for West Ham and Palace?

DERBY COUNTY

271. Can you name the Costa Rican striker who joined the Hammers from Derby County in July 1999?

272. Which former West Ham 'keeper was in goal for the Rams for the Hammers' 5-0 Premier League win at Pride Park in November 2007?

273. The Hammers' last Premier League meetings with Derby were in the 2007/08 season when the Rams were relegated with a record lowest points tally. How many points did they amass 11, 13 or 15?

274. In which season did the clubs first meet in the Premier League?

275. Can you recall the score from that first Premier League meeting?

276. Who was the first Hammer to score a Premier League goal against the Rams - Tony Cottee, Trevor Morley or Ian Bishop?

277. On three occasions the Hammers have scored four of more goals in Premier League matches against Derby County - true or false?

278. In the 1998/99 season West Ham registered a Premier League double over the Rams - can you recall the two scorelines?

279. Which defender left West Ham to join Derby on loan in 2007 before agreeing a permanent switch to the Rams?

280. Can you name the player who began his playing career with West Ham and his managerial career with Derby County?

281. Former West Ham boss Slaven Bilic played Premier League football for both West Ham and Everton - true or false?

282. Who scored his first two goals for West Ham in a 3-1 win at Goodison Park in the 2018/19 season?

283. West Ham began the calendar year of 1994 with a 1-0 New Year's Day victory over Everton at Goodison Park - can you recall the Hammers' scorer?

284. Who scored twice for the Hammers in their 3-1 victory over Everton in May 2018?

285. Can you name the Toffees' striker who netted a hat-trick against the Hammers in May 1999?

286. Which two managers have taken charge of both West Ham United and Everton in the Premier League?

287. Ahead of the 2019/20 season, the Hammers have yet to record a Premier League double over Everton - true or false?

288. Which West Ham manager secured his first Premier League win as Hammers boss with a 3-1 triumph at Goodison Park?

289. What nationality is former West Ham and Everton striker Nikica Jelavic?

290. At which club did Danish defender Lars Jacobson play more Premier League games - West Ham or Everton?

THE 1997/98 SEASON

291. In which position did West Ham end the 1997/98 Premier League - seventh, eighth or ninth?

292. The Hammers lost just two home league games in 1997/98. Can you name the two sides that won at the Boleyn Ground?

293. Which two clubs did West Ham record a Premier League double over in 1997/98?

294. Who ended the season as the club's leading Premier League scorer?

295. How many goals did the Hammers' leading scorer net in 1997/98?

296. Which two players came joint second in the scoring charts with seven league goals each?

297. Can you name the West Ham goalkeeper who marked his Premier League debut with a clean sheet against champions-elect Arsenal in March 1998?

298. How many Premier League goals did the Hammers score in 1997/98 - more than 55 goals, less than 55 goals or 55 goals exactly?

299. Which Premier League club knocked the Hammers out of both domestic cup competitions during the 1997/98 season?

300. Can you name the London club than ended the season bottom of the Premier League table?

FULHAM

301. What was the score when West Ham travelled to Fulham for a pre-season friendly in July 2019?

302. Can you name the midfielder who played Premier League football for both clubs before going on to manage Fulham?

303. In which season did the Hammers first face Fulham in the Premier League?

304. Can you name the French-born Mali international striker who scored West Ham's first Premier League goal against Fulham?

305. Who scored the final goal to wrap up the Hammers' 3-1 victory over Fulham at London Stadium in 2018/19?

306. Legendary West Ham defender Tony Gale, who played in the club's 1993/94 Premier League campaign, was originally signed from Fulham - true or false?

307. Kevin Nolan gave West Ham an early lead in their 3-0 victory over the Cottagers in September 2012. What was his opening goal timed at - 33 seconds, 43 seconds or 53 seconds?

308. Which striker began his senior career at Brighton before later playing in the Premier League with West Ham and Fulham?

309. Who was the unfortunate Fulham goalkeeper who scored an own goal to give West Ham a 2-1 win at Craven Cottage in September 2005?

310. The Hammers completed their first Premier League double over Fulham in 2002/03 - true or false?

HUDDERSFIELD TOWN

311. When West Ham faced Huddersfield in the Premier League in 2017/18, it was the first time the two clubs had met in the top flight of English football in the modern era - true or false?

312. Who was the Hammers' boss for their first Premier League meeting with Huddersfield Town?

313. West Ham's first Premier League victory of 2017/18 came against Huddersfield Town - true or false?

314. Who scored the Hammers' opening goal in their 2-0 win over the Terriers at London Stadium in September 2017?

315. West Ham recorded their most comprehensive away win of the 2017/18 season at Huddersfield - what was the final score?

316. The Hammers' visit to the John Smith's Stadium in January 2018 was their first ever match at that venue - true or false?

317. Who netted West Ham's second-half equaliser in their 1-1 draw away to Huddersfield Town in November 2018?

318. Can you name the West Ham striker who scored twice in the final six minutes as the Hammers came from 3-2 down to win 4-3 against Huddersfield in March 2019?

319. Who opened the scoring in that seven-goal thriller in 2018/19?

320. When the Hammers defeated Huddersfield Town 2-0 in September 2017 who was the goalkeeper who recorded his first clean sheet for the club?

HULL CITY

321. When was the last season that West Ham played Hull City in the Premier League?

322. In which Premier League season did West Ham first face Hull City?

323. Hull City have never ended a Premier League campaign above West Ham in the final table - true or false?

324. How many Premier League goals did Carlton Cole score for the Hammers against Hull City - was it two, three or four?

325. Which member of the Hammers' 2019/20 squad has previously played in the Premier League for Hull City?

326. Early in his playing career, Mark Noble played on loan for Hull City - true or false?

327. How many times have West Ham defeated Hull City in Premier League fixtures - four times, five times or six times?

328. Who is the only player to score for West Ham against Hull City at London Stadium?

329. What was the score when Hull played at the Boleyn Ground for the final time in January 2015?

330. Can you name the Senegalese international who left West Ham to join Hull City in September 2014?

IPSWICH TOWN

331. Can you name the striker who scored the Hammers' first Premier League goal against Ipswich before leaving West Ham to join the Suffolk cub?

332. West Ham United have never lost a Premier League match to Ipswich Town - true or false?

333. What was the fee that West Ham reportedly paid to sign Aaron Cresswell from Ipswich in July 2014?

334. Ipswich Town have yet to visit London Stadium - true or false?

335. Which former West Ham manager guided Ipswich Town to promotion in 1991/92 and managed them in the inaugural Premier League season?

336. Can you name the Danish international who scored for Ipswich in both of the 1-1 Premier League draws against the Hammers in 1994/95?

337. Which former West Ham trainee scored against the Hammers at Portman Road in October 2001?

338. West Ham won 3-2 at Portman Road in 2001/02 - who scored the Hammers' final goal in the 90th minute?

339. Who scored West Ham's opening goal against Ipswich Town in April 1994 and later joined Town's rivals Norwich City?

340. West Ham played Ipswich Town in a pre-season friendly ahead of the Hammers' 2018/19 Premier League campaign - what was the final score?

THE 1998/99 SEASON

341. The Hammers ended the 1998/99 season in fifth place. Which four sides finished above them that season?

342. Who was West Ham's only ever-present player in their 1998/99 Premier League campaign?

343. Ian Wright was the Hammers' leading league scorer in 1998/99 but how many goals did he score - nine, ten or eleven?

344. Which Cameroon international midfielder joined the Hammers in January 1999?

345. Striker John Hartson left the club in 1998/99, which Premier League rival did he join?

346. Can you name the goalkeeper who kept a clean sheet on his West Ham debut in the opening day win at Sheffield Wednesday?

347. From which club did the Hammers sign left-back Scott Minto during the 1998/99 season?

348. West Ham's fifth-place finish resulted in qualification to which European competition the following season?

349. Despite recording their highest ever Premier League finish, the side ended the campaign with a negative goal difference - true or false?

350. How many Premier League away matches did the Hammers win in 1998/99 - five, six or seven?

SAM ALLARDYCE

351. Sam's first permanent English managerial appointment was at Blackpool - true or false?

352. Where was Sam last managing prior to taking the reins at West Ham - Blackburn Rovers, Newcastle United or Bolton Wanderers?

353. In what year was Allardyce named West Ham manager?

354. Sam guided West Ham to Premier League promotion in this first season at the club - true or false?

355. Which league position did Sam guide the Hammers to in his first Premier League campaign with the club?

356. February 2014 saw Sam named the Premier League's Manager of the Month, how many league games did the Hammers win that month - three, four or five?

357. Against which club did Sam win his first Premier League match as Hammers boss?

358. In which Premier League position did the Hammers finish in Sam's final season in charge at the Boleyn Ground?

359. Who provided the opposition for Allardyce's final game as West Ham boss?

360. Which Premier League club did Sam manage after leaving West Ham?

JACK WILSHERE

361. From which club did the Hammers sign Jack Wilshere in the summer of 2018?

362. In the 2009/10 season which Premier League side did Jack join on loan?

363. In which Premier League campaign did Wilshere spend the season on loan at Bournemouth?

364. Who was the Hammers' manger when Wilshere joined the club?

365. What length of contract did Wilshere agree when he arrived at London Stadium?

366. Against which club did Wilshere make his Hammers' debut?

367. What squad number was Wilshere given for the Hammers 2019/20 Premier League campaign?

368. How many Premier League fixtures did Jack feature in for the Hammers in 2018/19 - was it eight, 18 or 28?

369. Who were the opposition when Wilshere tasted his first Premier League victory as a West Ham player?

370. As at the start of the 2019/20 campaign, how many full England caps has Jack won?

LEEDS UNITED

371. In which season did the Hammers last face Leeds United in the Premier League?

372. Who became the then world's most expensive defender when he transferred from West Ham to Leeds in November 2000?

373. West Ham failed to score in their first four Premier League matches against Leeds United - true or false?

374. Who scored a brace for the Hammers in a 2-2 draw at Elland Road in 1994?

375. Which West Ham striker opened the scoring in a 3-0 victory over Leeds at the Boleyn Ground in the 1997/98 season?

376. In May 1999 the Hammers had three players sent off in their Premier League match with Leeds United - can you recall the three players who saw red?

377. Who was the referee that brandished the three red cards in the above match?

378. In the 2000/01 season which West Ham defender struck on the stroke of half time to give the Hammers their only Premier League victory at Elland Road?

379. David Moyes has managed both West Ham United and Leeds United - true or false?

380. How many goals were scored when Leeds last visited the Boleyn Ground for a Premier League fixture - five, six or seven?

LEICESTER CITY

381. Can you name the striker who scored the Premier League's first ever goal in 1992 and later played for both the Foxes and the Hammers?

382. In Leicester City's 2015/16 title-winning season, what were the two results from their matches against the Hammers?

383. In which season did West Ham first face Leicester City as Premier League opponents?

384. Which West Ham player was sent off in the 1-1 draw away to Leicester City in 2018/19?

385. Ahead of the 2019/20 season, how many times have West Ham registered a Premier League double over the Foxes?

386. Which venue hosted the first Premier League meeting between the two clubs - the Boleyn Ground or Filbert Street?

387. Hammers legend Tony Cottee once scored two goals for Leicester City in a Premier League game against West Ham - true or false?

388. Who was the first West Ham player to score a Premier League goal against the Foxes - Steve Lomas, Julian Dicks or Frank Lampard (Jnr)?

389. Midfielder John Paintsil has played for both clubs. What nationality is he?

390. Which West Ham player was on target for both teams in the Hammers' 3-2 Premier League victory over Leicester in November 1998?

LIVERPOOL

391. Who scored West Ham's equaliser in the 1-1 draw with Liverpool at London Stadium in February 2019?

392. West Ham began the calendar year of 2016 with a 2-0 win at home to Liverpool, can you name the former Reds striker who was on target for the Hammers in this game?

393. Can you name the Hammers keeper who kept a clean sheet in a 3-0 Premier League victory at Anfield in August 2015?

394. Which Hammer was on target but later sent off in the 3-0 win at Liverpool in 2015?

395. In which season did the Hammers first defeat Liverpool in the Premier League?

396. Can you name the former Liverpool player who scored twice in a 3-0 win for the Hammers at the Boleyn Ground in 1995?

397. In May 1998, the Hammers suffered a 5-0 defeat at Anfield. Can you name the former Hammer who netted Liverpool's final goal?

398. Ahead of the 2019/20 season, who was the last West Ham manager to oversee a Premier League victory over Liverpool?

399. Other than West Ham and Liverpool, which other three Premier League clubs did Glen Johnson represent?

400. Liverpool and which five other clubs have been ever-present members of the Premier League?

MANCHESTER CITY

401. Signed from Villarreal in the summer of 2019, who made his Hammers debut as a substitute in the opening game of the 2019/20 season against Manchester City?

402. What was the final score from Manchester City's final match at the Boleyn Ground in 2015/16?

403. Who was the last West Ham player to score against Manchester City at the Boleyn Ground?

404. Prior to the 2019/20 season, when did the Hammers last defeat Manchester City in a Premier League fixture?

405. Which player scored West Ham's winning goal in the above match?

406. Can you name the Welsh international striker who left West Ham to join Manchester City in January 2009?

407. Who has managed both West Ham and Manchester City in the Premier League?

408. At which four venues have Premier League fixtures between West Ham and Manchester City taken place?

409. In which season did the two clubs first meet as Premier League rivals?

410. Manchester City have been ever-present members of the Premier League - true or false?

THE 1999/2000 SEASON

411. The Intertoto Cup resulted in a short break between seasons. How many days passed between the end of 1998/99 and the Hammers' first Intertoto Cup game in 1999/2000 - 62 days, 64 days or 66 days?

412. Who were the Hammers' first Intertoto Cup opponents in 1999/2000?

413. Success in the Intertoto Cup resulted in qualification for which European competition?

414. Who netted the Hammers' first Premier League goal of the season to secure an 1-0 opening day victory?

415. Against which Yorkshire club did West Ham register their first Premier League away win of the 1999/2000 season?

416. Who scored the only goal of the game to give West Ham a 1-0 home win over Liverpool in November 1999?

417. How many Premier League goals did the Hammers score in 1999/2000 - 50, 51 or 52?

418. What was the club's Premier League points total in 1999/2000 - 55, 57 or 59?

419. Who was the Hammers' leading Premier League scorer in 1999/2000?

420. West Ham ended the 1999/2000 campaign in the top half of the Premier League table - true or false?

MANCHESTER UNITED

421. Which club did David Moyes first take charge of
- West Ham or Manchester United?

422. The Hammers have yet to end a Premier League
campaign above Manchester United - true or false?

423. Can you name the Argentinean forward who played Premier
League football for both West Ham and Manchester United?

424. Who scored the Hammers' winning goal in the final
game at the Boleyn Ground as West Ham beat
Manchester United 3-2 in May 2016?

425. In which season did the Hammers register their only
Premier League double over Manchester United?

426. Who netted the only goal of the game to give the
Hammers a 1-0 victory at Old Trafford in December 2001?

427. Can you name the West Ham 'keeper who kept
a clean sheet in both Premier League games against
Manchester United in 2006/07?

428. What was the score when Manchester United first
visited London Stadium?

429. Can you name the Manchester United defender
who put the ball into his own net when the Hammers
won 3-1 at London Stadium in 2018/19?

430. Why was the final day 1-1 draw between West Ham
and Manchester United at the Boleyn Ground
in 1994/95 so costly for the Red Devils?

MIDDLESBROUGH

431. Which Northern Ireland striker netted the Hammers' second goal in their 2-0 home win over Boro in March 1996?

432. Only once have the Hammers faced Boro at Ayresome Park in a Premier League fixture - true or false?

433. Which club has spent more seasons in the Premier League - West Ham or Boro?

434. In which season did the Hammers record their most recent Premier League double over Boro?

435. Can you name the West Ham striker who bagged a brace in the 3-1 win at the Riverside in January 2017?

436. Which goalkeeper left London Stadium to join Middlesbrough in July 2017?

437. Can you name the midfielder who scored for Boro against the Hammers in May 2009 and then joined West Ham in January 2011?

438. Who was the first West Ham player to score a Premier League goal against Middlesbrough?

439. Can you name the West Ham player who netted a wonder solo effort against Boro at the London Stadium in October 2016?

440. In the 1996/97 season both clubs were relegated from the Premier League - true or false?

SEBASTIEN HALLER

441. From which club did the Hammers sign Haller in July 2019?

442. What was the reported fee that the Hammers paid for him?

443. His transfer fee set a new club record - true or false?

444. What nationality is Haller?

445. With which French club did he begin his professional career?

446. Which Dutch club did he join on loan before completing a permanent transfer?

447. How many goals has Haller scored as an Under-21 international - 13, 23 of 33?

448. In 2018/19 how many Bundesliga goals did Haller score - 15, 17 or 19?

449. Haller's first goal for the Hammers came in a pre-season friendly against which German club?

450. Against which club did Haller make his Premier League debut?

NEWCASTLE UNITED

451. When West Ham travel to St James' Park in 2019/20, it will be their longest trip of the season - true or false?

452. Other than West Ham and Newcastle, can you name Craig Bellamy's five other Premier League clubs?

453. Which Premier League club did Andy Carroll play for in-between his time at Newcastle and West Ham?

454. What fee did the Hammers pay to Newcastle for Scott Parker in June 2007?

455. When did the two clubs last compete against one another outside of the Premier League?

456. Can you name the West Ham legend who managed the club for its first Premier League match against Newcastle?

457. Which West Ham defender took the mantle of scoring the club's first Premier League goal against Newcastle - Steve Potts, Alvin Martin or Tim Breacker?

458. Can you name the future Hammer who netted two goals for Newcastle against West Ham at the Boleyn Ground in March 1994?

459. In which season did the Hammers record their first Premier League double over Newcastle?

460. Who opened the scoring for West Ham in the 2-0 victory over Newcastle at London Stadium in 2018/19?

461. Which West Ham defender left the club in the summer of 2019 to join Premier League rivals Norwich City?

462. Can you name the member of the Hammers' 2019/20 Premier League squad that was once voted the Canaries' Player of the Season?

463. Former West Ham striker Craig Bellamy began his career with Norwich City - true or false?

464. In August 2006, which goalkeeper did the Hammers sign from Norwich City?

465. In which season did the two clubs first meet in the Premier League?

466. The 2019/20 campaign signalled the Canaries' first visit to London Stadium - true or false?

467. Ahead of the 2019/20 season, how many times have West Ham beaten Norwich City in the Premier League?

468. Who netted a last-gasp West Ham equaliser to salvage a 2-2 draw at home to Norwich City in September 2015?

469. Which former West Ham full-back later managed Norwich City in the Premier League?

470. Despite both clubs being in the Premier League in 2015/16, the Hammers and Canaries played one another in a pre-season friendly - true or false?

THE 2000/01 SEASON

471. How many games into the season were the Hammers when they won their first Premier League game of 2000/01 - seven, eight or nine?

472. Against which club did the first league victory arrive?

473. In which league position did the Hammers end the 2000/01 campaign?

474. Can you name the three 'Cities' that suffered relegation from the Premier League in 2000/01?

475. In which month of the season did West Ham record their first home league win - September, October or November?

476. Against which club was that first home league triumph recorded?

477. Who scored the Hammers' first Premier League goal of 2000/01 in the opening day London derby at Chelsea?

478. Whose eleven Premier League goals in 2000/01 saw him end the season as the club's leading league goalscorer?

479. Who departed as the club's manager with one game of the season remaining?

480. Can you name the club's caretaker-manager for the final game of the season away to Middlesbrough?

BOBBY DAZZLER

Bobby Zamora netted the only goal of the game as West Ham defeated Preston North End in the 2004/05 Play-Off final to win promotion to the Premier League. Can you name Bobby's ten promotion-winning teammates? (4-4-2 with Zamora in attack)

481. Goalkeeper? (five letters/six letters)

482. Right-back? (five letters/five letters)

483. Left-back? (five letters/six letters)

484. Central defence? (seven letters/four letters)

485. Central defence? (five letters/nine letters)

486. Central midfield? (five letters/eight letters)

487. Right midfield? (five letters/six letters)

488. Central midfielder? (six letters/seven letters)

489. Striker? (six letters/eight letters)

490. Left midfield? (seven letters/eleven letters)

491. In how many seasons have the Hammers and Nottingham Forest been Premier League rivals?

492. In which season did the two clubs last meet in a Premier League fixture?

493. What was the score the last time West Ham played Forest in the Premier League?

494. Which Welsh left-back scored his one and only West Ham Premier League goal to open the scoring in a 2-0 win at the City Ground in September 1996?

495. Can you name the West Ham defender who was sent off in the 2-0 win away to Forest in 1996/97?

496. Who did the Hammers sign from Nottingham Forest in November 2003 for a fee of £500,000?

497. Can you name the left-back who has played for both West Ham and Forest, managed Forest and been on the coaching staff at West Ham?

498. Striker Stan Collymore has played in the Premier League for both West Ham and Forest - true or false?

499. Which Hammers' crowd favourite was on target against Forest when the two sides drew 1-1 in the Premier League in April 1995?

500. Ahead of the 2019/20 season, Nottingham Forest had yet to visit London Stadium - true or false?

OLDHAM ATHLETIC

501. Oldham Athletic were inaugural members of the Premier League - true or false?

502. In how many seasons have Oldham competed in the Premier League?

503. West Ham and Oldham have only faced one another in one Premier League season - which campaign was it that they came up against one another?

504. Can you name the Hammers striker who scored in both Premier League games against the Latics?

505. Who opened the scoring for West Ham in their first Premier League meeting with Oldham - Alvin Martin, Tony Cottee or Ian Bishop?

506. Can you name the Hammers goalkeeper who kept a clean sheet in the first Premier League meeting between the two clubs?

507. Who was the Hammers' manager when they played both their Premier League games against Oldham?

508. Can you name the former England striker who managed Oldham in their Premier League meetings with West Ham?

509. The Hammers boast a 100% winning record in Premier League games against Oldham - true or false?

510. How many goals were scored in total in the two Premier League meetings between the two clubs - five, seven or nine?

PORTSMOUTH

511. Which England goalkeeper played Premier League football for both West Ham and Portsmouth?

512. Who has managed both the Hammers and Pompey in the Premier League?

513. In which season did the Hammers last face Portsmouth in the Premier League?

514. Who was the last Hammers player to score a Premier League goal against Pompey?

515. In consecutive seasons, 2008/09 and 2009/10, the Hammers faced Portsmouth away on Boxing Day - true or false?

516. Can you recall the score from the first Premier League match between the two clubs in December 2005?

517. Who scored the Hammers' first Premier League goal against Portsmouth - Shaun Newton, James Collins or Bobby Zamora?

518. Can you name the Portsmouth goalscorer who netted their first Premier League goal against the Hammers and later in his career played for West Ham?

519. Can you name the midfielder who left West Ham to join Portsmouth in January 2009?

520. In which Premier League season were the Hammers doubled by Pompey - 2006/07, 2007/08 or 2008/09?

CAPTAIN CALLING

Mark Noble skippered West Ham to a historic 3-2 Premier League victory over Manchester United in the club's final match at the Boleyn Ground in May 2016. Can you name Noble's ten teammates from that emotional evening? (3-5-2 with Noble in central midfield)

521. Goalkeeper? (six letters/eight letters)

522. Right side defender? (seven letters/four letters)

523. Central defender? (six letters/seven letters)

524. Left side defender? (five letters/nine letters)

525. Central midfielder? (eight letters/seven letters)

526. Central midfielder? (six letters/seven letters)

527. Right side midfielder? (seven letters/seven letters)

528. Striker? (four letters/seven letters)

529. Striker? (six letters/five letters)

530. Left side midfielder? (seven letters/five letters)

531. Who was named the Hammers' new manager ahead of the 2001/02 season?

532. Can you name the only West Ham player to be ever-present throughout the 2001/02 Premier League campaign?

533. Which two players shared goalkeeping duties for the Hammers in 2001/02?

534. In what position did the team finish in the Premier League in 2001/02?

535. Who were the Hammers' shirt sponsors in 2001/02?

536. Which company produced the West Ham kit for their 2001/02 Premier League campaign?

537. Who received the Hammer of the Year award in 2001/02?

538. Against which London club did the Hammers share eight goals in a remarkable 4-4 draw in November 2001?

539. Which club did West Ham beat 4-0 at the Boleyn Ground on Boxing Day 2001?

540. Who did the Hammers defeat 2-1 on the final day of the 2001/02 Premier League season?

QUEENS PARK RANGERS

541. Which striker has twice scored the winning goal in a Play-Off final to secure Premier League promotion for both West Ham and QPR?

542. Who won a hat-trick of Hoops' Player of the Season awards before crossing London to join the Hammers in 1997?

543. Other than the Hammers and the Hoops, which other team has Trevor Sinclair played Premier League football for?

544. Can you name the former West Ham player who later managed QPR in the Premier League?

545. At the start of the 1995/96 season, the Hammers played four home fixtures at Loftus Road due to the redevelopment work that was on ongoing at the Boleyn Ground - true or false?

546. In which season did the two sides last meet in the Premier League?

547. Who is the only West Ham 'keeper to record two Premier League clean sheets in a season against QPR?

548. West Ham won their first Premier League fixture against QPR in 1995/96. Who scored the Hammers' goal in that 1-0 home win?

549. When the Hammers won 2-1 away to QPR in 2012/13, who fired them in front after just three minutes?

550. QPR have never registered a Premier League double over the Hammers - true or false?

READING

551. In which season did Alan Pardew quit Reading to take charge at West Ham?

552. After making his Premier League debut for West Ham in 2015 which youngster joined Reading on loan in 2017?

553. Can you name the goalkeeper who started his career in England with Reading and later made over a century of Premier League appearances for the Hammers?

554. In how many Premier League campaigns have the Hammers come face-to-face with Reading?

555. Who scored a hat-trick for the Hammers in their last Premier League match against Reading?

556. What was the final score when the two sides last met in a Premier League fixture?

557. In which season did the Hammers first play Reading in the Premier League?

558. Can you name the West Ham player who netted a second-half brace in the 3-0 win at the Madejski Stadium in 2007/08?

559. Who was the Hammers' marksman in the 1-1 draw with the Royals on Boxing Day 2007?

560. Which former West Ham coach, under Gianfranco Zola, later managed Reading?

SHEFFIELD UNITED

561. Sheffield United were the first of the three promoted clubs that West Ham faced in 2019/20 - true or false?

562. Prior to the 2019/20 Premier League fixtures with the Blades, in which competition did the two sides last meet?

563. Can you name the former Hammer who joined the Blades in the summer of 2019?

564. Ahead of the 2019/20 campaign, when did the Hammers and Blades last face one another in the Premier League?

565. The 2019/20 campaign will be the third season that the two clubs have met in the Premier League - when was the first?

566. Who scored the Hammers' goal in a 1-0 victory over the Blades in November 2006?

567. Can you recall the West Ham 'keeper who kept a clean sheet in the home win over the Blades in 2006/07?

568. Honours ended even when the two clubs first met in a Premier League match. What was the final score - 0-0, 1-1 or 2-2?

569. Who managed Sheffield United in their first Premier League match against the Hammers?

570. Can you name the West Ham midfielder who had a stint at Sheffield United sandwiched in between two spells with the Hammers?

THE 2002/03 SEASON

571. The 2002/03 season saw the Hammers suffer relegation
     - how many consecutive seasons had they enjoyed
     in the Premier League?

572. Can you name the two other clubs that were also relegated?

573. Following boss Glenn Roeder's illness, who took charge
     of team affairs?

574. How many points did the Hammers win in 2002/03
     - 40, 41 or 42?

575. The Hammers' points tally set a record for a relegated
     team in a 38-game Premier League season - true or false?

576. Who ended the season as top league scorer?

577. Can you recall the price of a West Ham home
     programme in 2002/03?

578. In which month did West Ham record their first home
     Premier League victory of the 2002/03 campaign?

579. Who were the final club that the Hammers beat in 2002/03?

580. On which ground did the season end with a 2-2 draw?

SHEFFIELD WEDNESDAY

581. Who joined the Hammers from Sheffield Wednesday in January 1999?

582. Which member of the West Ham squad for 2019/20 has previously played for Sheffield Wednesday?

583. Can you name the former Sheffield Wednesday goalkeeper who later in his career was goalkeeper coach at West Ham?

584. West Ham won their first Premier League match with Sheffield Wednesday 2-0 in 1993/94 - who scored both goals for the Hammers?

585. Who was the Hammers' hat-trick hero in the 5-1 victory over the Owls at the Boleyn Ground in May 1997?

586. Overshadowed by the hat-trick hero, who grabbed a brace in that 5-1 win?

587. In 1999/2000 the Hammers and Owls produced a seven-goal thriller at the Boleyn Ground, West ham won the game but what was the final score - 6-1, 4-3 or 5-2?

588. In which season did the two clubs last meet as Premier League rivals?

589. In how many Premier League seasons have the Hammers faced the Owls - five, six or seven?

590. The Hammers won for the first time at Hillsborough in the Premier League in October 1995 - who netted in this 1-0 away win?

SOUTHAMPTON

591. Who scored a second-half brace in December 2018 as the Hammers came from behind to win at Southampton?

592. Can you name the West Ham defender who scored his first Premier League goal for the club in the 3-0 home win over the Saints in 2018/19?

593. Harry Redknapp and Alan Pardew have managed both West Ham and Southampton in the Premier League - true or false?

594. In which season did the two clubs first meet in the Premier League?

595. Who was the first Hammer to score a Premier League goal against Southampton - Martin Allen, Trevor Morley or Lee Chapman?

596. What was the name of Southampton's former ground which hosted the first ever Premier League meeting between the two clubs?

597. West Ham ended the calendar year of 2015 with a 2-1 home win over Southampton - who scored the Hammers' winner?

598. In which season did the Hammers record their first Premier League double over Southampton - 1998/99, 1999/2000 or 2000/01?

599. Can you name the Northern Ireland international striker who had a spell with the Saints in between two stints at the Boleyn Ground?

600. Which venue will host the first 2019/20 Premier League fixture between the two clubs - London Stadium or St Mary's?

THE 2005/06 SEASON

601. Who did the Hammers defeat in the Play-Off final to win promotion to the Premier League for 2005/06?

602. West Ham enjoyed a winning start to life back in the Premier League, what was the score in their opening day match with Blackburn Rovers?

603. Who was the Hammers' manager in 2005/06?

604. Against which club did the Hammers suffer their first Premier League defeat of the 2005/06 season?

605. Can you name the striker West Ham signed from Norwich City in January 2006?

606. Which company were the Hammers' shirt sponsors in 2005/06?

607. In which position did the Hammers end their first season back in the Premier League?

608. West Ham had no ever-present players in the 2005/06 Premier League campaign - true or false?

609. Who ended the season as runner-up in the Hammer of the Year award?

610. Marlon Harewood was the Hammers' leading Premier League scorer in 2005/06. How many goals did he score - 14, 15 or 16?

QUIZ 62
STOKE CITY

611. Which popular West Ham winger left the club to join Stoke City in January 2009?

612. Can you name the England international defender who has played Premier League Football for the Hammers and the Potters?

613. Victor Moses has played on loan for both West Ham and Stoke but which Premier League club was he on loan from?

614. Former West Ham player and coach Kevin Keen also played for Stoke City - true or false?

615. What was the then club record fee that West Ham paid to Stoke City for Marko Arnautovic in July 2017?

616. In which season did West Ham face Stoke City in the Premier League, the League Cup and the FA Cup?

617. Can you recall the season that the two clubs were first Premier League rivals?

618. The Hammers completed a double over the Potters the first season they met in a Premier League campaign - true or false?

619. Who scored the Hammers' goal in their 1-0 win away to Stoke City in March 2013?

620. Can you name the Hammers striker who scored a last-minute equaliser in the 1-1 draw with Stoke at London Stadium in April 2018?

621. On each of the two occasions that the Hammers have suffered relegation from the Premier League, Sunderland have been relegated alongside them - true or false?

622. On which venue did the first Sunderland v West Ham United Premier League fixture take place - Roker Park or the Stadium of Light?

623. Which two managers have taken charge of West Ham and Sunderland in the Premier League?

624. In which season did the two sides first meet in the Premier League?

625. What was the score in the first Premier League match between the two clubs?

626. Who was the first West Ham player to score a Premier League goal against Sunderland?

627. What was the transfer fee the Hammers paid to Sunderland for Don Hutchison in the summer of 2001?

628. Who netted the Hammers' last-minute goal to secure a 1-0 win over the Black Cats on their first visit to London Stadium?

629. In which season were West Ham and Sunderland Premier League rivals and also paired with one another in the FA Cup?

630. Which future Sunderland striker netted the Hammers' third goal in the 3-0 victory over the Black Cats at the Boleyn Ground in April 2002?

THE 2006/07 SEASON

631. Against which newly-promoted club did the Hammers secure their first away point of the 2006/07 season?

632. Which Italian side knocked the Hammers out of the UEFA Cup?

633. Against which club did the Hammers suffer their first Premier League defeat of the season - Newcastle United, Liverpool or Manchester City?

634. Can you name the leader of the Icelandic consortium that took control of the club in November 2006?

635. Who was dismissed as West Ham United manager during the 2006/07 campaign?

636. Which former West Ham player became manager in December 2006?

637. Bobby Zamora ended the season as the Hammers' leading Premier League scorer, how many goals did he score - eleven, 13 or 15?

638. In which league position did the Hammers end the 2006/07 season?

639. Can you name the three clubs that were relegated from the Premier League in 2006/07?

640. Who was voted Hammer of the Year in 2006/07?

AVRAM GRANT

641. What nationality is former West Ham manager Avram Grant?

642. Who did Grant replace as West Ham boss?

643. Ahead of which season was did Grant become Hammers' boss?

644. Who was Grant's first signing as West Ham manager?

645. Against which club did Grant secure his first Premier League point as West Ham boss?

646. Who did the Hammers beat 1-0 at the Boleyn Ground as Grant celebrated his first Premier League win in charge of West Ham?

647. At which club was Grant previously managing before joining the Hammers?

648. Which was the first Premier League club that Grant managed?

649. Who were the Hammers' Premier League opposition for Grant's final match as West Ham boss?

650. Who replaced Grant as West Ham manager in the summer of 2011?

651. Who were the Hammers' first Welsh opponents in the Premier League - Swansea City or Cardiff City?

652. Prior to the first Premier League meeting with Swansea in 2012/13, when did the Hammers last face the Swans in a league fixture - 1980/81, 1981/82 or 1982/83?

653. What was the final score when the Hammers first hosted a Premier League match against Swansea City?

654. Which member of the Hammers' 2019/20 Premier League squad joined the club from Swansea in the summer of 2018?

655. Who netted the Hammers' last-minute winner against the Swans at London Stadium in September 2017?

656. Can you recall who scored the Hammers' late consolation goal in the 4-1 reverse at the Liberty Stadium in 2017/18?

657. Which Ghanaian international did the Hammers sign from Swansea for a fee of £20.5M in August 2016?

658. On Boxing Day 2016, the Hammers enjoyed an emphatic Premier League victory away to Swansea - what was the final score?

659. Who was the first West Ham manager to oversee a Premier League victory at the Liberty Stadium?

660. In which season did the Hammers record their first Premier League double over the Swans?

QUIZ 67
ALAN CURBISHLEY

661. Where was Alan born in November 1957?

662. How many league games did Alan play for the Hammers
   - over 100, under 100 or 100 exactly?

663. With which club did Alan begin his managerial career?

664. Prior to becoming West Ham manager, Alan spent
   a brief period as a television pundit - true or false?

665. In which season did Curbishley return to West Ham
   as manager?

666. Who did the Hammers beat 1-0 in Curbishley's first
   game in charge?

667. Can you name the player that scored the first Premier
   League goal of Curbishley's reign as West Ham manager?

668. Alan Curbishley was the West Ham boss that signed
   striker Dean Ashton - true or false?

669. Prior to Alan Curbishley, who was the last player
   to return to the club as manager?

670. Who replaced Alan as West Ham boss in 2008?

THE 2007/08 SEASON

671. Who was West Ham boss in 2007/08?

672. Dean Ashton ended the season as top scorer with twelve goals but how many of his dozen were scored in the Premier League?

673. Other than the Hammers, how many London clubs competed in the Premier League in 2007/08?

674. How many Premier League points did the Hammers amass in 2007/08 - 47, 48 or 49?

675. In which position did they finish in the final Premier League table?

676. Who were the club's two ever-present players in their 2007/08 Premier League campaign?

677. In which round of the FA Cup were West Ham knocked out by Manchester City in 2007/08?

678. Which fellow Premier League club eliminated the Hammers from the League Cup in 2007/08?

679. Can you name the Scottish defender who left the Hammers to join Glasgow Rangers in the 2007/08 season?

680. The Hammers ended the season with a 2-2 draw at home to which club?

BILLY BONDS

681. A true West Ham legend but with which London club did Billy begin his playing career?

682. After retiring as a player, which West Ham manager appointed Billy as the club's youth coach?

683. In 1989 Billy made an unsuccessful application to become West Ham manager - who did the club opt to appoint?

684. Billy Bonds is the first West Ham manager to have guided the club to promotion to the Premier League - true or false?

685. Taking charge of the Hammers in the Premier League in 1993/94, in which position did the club end the season?

686. Who was Billy's first choice goalkeeper when he managed the club's 1993/94 Premier League campaign?

687. Can you name Billy's West Ham captain who left the club early in the 1993/94 season?

688. Who were the opposition for Billy Bonds' final game as West Ham boss?

689. Who replaced Billy Bonds as West Ham manager?

690. After leaving West Ham, which club did Bonds then become manager of?

SWINDON TOWN

691. Swindon Town have only spent one season in the Premier League - true or false?

692. In which season did the Hammers first face Swindon as Premier League rivals?

693. Which ground hosted the first Premier League meeting between the two clubs - the Boleyn Ground or the County Ground?

694. What was the score when the Hammers first played Swindon in a Premier League fixture?

695. Who was Swindon boss for their first Premier League meeting with West Ham?

696. Can you name the Hammers manager who oversaw the club's first Premier League match with Swindon?

697. The second Premier League meeting between the two clubs ended 1-1. Can you name the Hammers scorer?

698. Which of the three following Swindon players was on target in that 1-1 draw - Martin Ling, Jan-Aage Fjortoft or Keith Scott?

699. When the Hammers and Swindon first met in the Premier League it was both clubs' debut season as members of the Premier League - true or false?

700. Which former West Ham striker was loaned to Swindon Town from Celtic and made seven Premier League appearances for the Robins?

701. West Ham began their 2008/09 Premier League campaign with a 2-1 win over which club?

702. Who netted the Hammers' first goal of the 2008/09 season?

703. On which ground did West Ham register their first Premier League away win of 2008/09?

704. Can you name the former Hammer who made a goalscoring return to the Boleyn Ground with his new side in January 2009?

705. Carlton Cole ended the season as the Hammers' leading scorer - from which club did West Ham sign him?

706. In which month of the 2008/09 season was Gianfranco Zola appointed the club's manager?

707. Which London rival attracted the biggest crowd of the season to the Boleyn Ground in 2008/09 - Arsenal, Chelsea or Tottenham Hotspur?

708. Who were the club's kit manufacturer in 2008/09?

709. Which player was ever-present in the Premier League season and voted runner-up in the Hammer of the Year award?

710. West Ham ended the 2008/09 season in the top half of the Premier League table - true or false?

JOE COLE

711. Joe Cole was born on 8 November but in what year?

712. Where in London was Joe born?

713. In which season did Joe make his Premier League debut for West Ham?

714. Who were the Hammers facing when Joe made his Premier League debut?

715. Joe's first taste of Premier League action came as a half-time substitute, who did he replace - Frank Lampard (Jnr), Trevor Sinclair or Eyal Berkovic?

716. Cole's first Premier League goal came against Bradford City in February 2000 - can you recall the final score from the game?

717. Joe made his full England debut while still a West Ham player - true or false?

718. Which club did Joe join when he left West Ham in the summer of 2003?

719. Other than the Hammers, can you name the three other clubs that Joe has played Premier League football for?

720. When Joe returned to West Ham in 2013, against which club did he score the first Premier League goal of his second spell at the Boleyn Ground?

ALAN PARDEW

721. In his playing career, at which club did Alan make his Football League debut?

722. During his spell at which London club did he score 24 league goals?

723. In which season did Alan play in the FA Cup final?

724. Can you recall in which season Alan became West Ham manager?

725. In his first season as boss, Pardew led the Hammers to promotion - true or false?

726. What position did Pardew lead the Hammers to in his first campaign as a Premier League manager?

727. Which future England international striker did Alan sign from Norwich City in January 2006?

728. Against which club did the Hammers suffer a 4-0 Premier League defeat in what proved to be Alan's final match as West Ham boss?

729. Who succeeded Alan as West Ham manager?

730. Other than West Ham United, can you name the other clubs that Alan has managed in the Premier League?

THE 2009/10 SEASON

731. Who did the Hammers defeat in their opening game of the 2009/10 season?

732. How many Premier League away fixtures did the Hammers win in 2009/10?

733. Who netted the club's first Premier League goal in 2009/10 - Scott Parker, Kieron Dyer or Mark Noble?

734. In 2009/10, who was the Hammers' only ever-present player in the Premier League, League Cup and FA Cup fixtures?

735. The 2009/10 season saw West Ham complete Premier League doubles over London rivals Arsenal and Chelsea - true or false?

736. Who ended the season as the club's leading scorer with ten Premier League goals?

737. The Hammers ended the season in 17th place - can you name the three clubs who finished below them and were relegated?

738. How many Premier League points did West Ham amass in 2009/10 - 33, 34 or 35?

739. Which club did West Ham United face as a Premier League rival for the first time in 2009/10?

740. At the end of a frustrating season, who left his position as Hammers boss in May 2010?

741. A which London club did Glenn begin his professional playing career?

742. In an impressive playing career did Glenn ever play for West Ham?

743. Which club did he captain in the 1982 FA Cup final?

744. At which club was Glenn player/manager in 1992/93?

745. Which England manager appointed Roeder as a coach of the national team?

746. Who was the West Ham boss that lured Glenn back into club football when he was appointed Hammers coach?

747. In what year did Roeder take up his coaching role at the Boleyn Ground?

748. Roeder became the club's manager in the summer of 2001. What Premier League position did he guide the Hammers to in his first full season at the helm?

749. Other than West Ham United, which other club has Roeder managed in the Premier League?

750. Which Championship club did Glenn manage from October 2007 to January 2009?

DECLAN RICE

751. In what year was Declan Rice born?

752. Where in London was Rice born?

753. At the academy of which London-based Premier League club did he begin his junior career?

754. In which season did Declan make his Premier League debut for the Hammers?

755. Against which club did West Ham win 2-1 when Declan made his debut?

756. Rice's first two Premier League outings were as a substitute, against which club did he make his first league start for the Hammers?

757. Against which club did Rice score his first Premier League goal for West Ham?

758. Prior to Declan, who was the last player to make 50 appearances for the Hammers while still a teenager?

759. Rice was voted runner-up in the Hammer of the Year award in 2017/18, who pipped him to the award?

760. Against which country did Rice make his England debut in March 2019?

THE 2010/11 SEASON

761. A tough season for the Hammers, which two clubs were relegated alongside them in 2010/11?

762. Who was the Hammers' leading Premier League goalscorer in 2010/11 - Demba Ba or Carlton Cole?

763. How many league goals did the top scorer net in 2010/11 - seven, eight or nine?

764. Despite a poor Premier League campaign the Hammers reached which stage of the League Cup?

765. Which club finally ended the Hammers' League Cup campaign?

766. Who was presented with the Hammer of the Year award at the end of the 2010/11 campaign?

767. Goalkeeper Robert Green missed one Premier League match in 2010/11 - who replaced him for the fixture away to Blackburn in December 2010?

768. Can you name the former Hammer who netted Liverpool's consolation strike in their 3-1 defeat at the Boleyn Ground in 2010/11?

769. What was the price of a West Ham home programme for Premier League fixtures in 2010/11?

770. Who was appointed as West Ham's new manager in June 2011 and charged with returning the club to the Premier League?

771. Other than the Hammers which other Premier League club did Slaven play for?

772. From which club did West Ham sign him in 1996?

773. When Bilic joined the club his transfer fee set a new club record for an incoming player - true or false?

774. What was the fee that the Hammers paid for him?

775. Who was the Hammers' boss that signed him?

776. How many Premier League goals did he score in his West Ham career - two, four or six?

777. Which national side did he manage before taking charge at West Ham?

778. Ahead of which Premier League campaign was Slaven Bilic appointed manager of West Ham United?

779. Against which club did Slaven win his first match as a Premier League manager?

780. In which position did the Hammers end their first Premier League campaign under Bilic's management?

PABLO ZABALETA

781. On how many occasions was Pablo Zabaleta a Premier League champion with Manchester City?

782. Manuel Pellegrini was the manager who signed Pablo for Manchester City - true or false?

783. How many caps has Zabaleta won for Argentina - over 50, under 50 or 50 exactly?

784. What squad number was Pablo handed at West Ham for the 2019/20 season?

785. Ahead of which Premier League season did Zabaleta join the Hammers?

786. Who was the West Ham boss that signed Pablo?

787. Against which club did he make his Premier League debut for West Ham United?

788. How many Premier League appearances did Pablo make in his first season with the Hammers - 35, 36 or 37?

789. Which Spanish club was Zabaleta playing for before he came to England?

790. Can you name the Argentinean club that he began his career with?

THE 2012/13 SEASON

791. West Ham's 2012/13 campaign saw them return to the Premier League after an absence of how many seasons?

792. Can you name the Hammers' midfielder who spent the 2012/13 season on loan with Birmingham City?

793. Defender George McCartney joined the Hammers in the summer of 2012 after making his loan move from which Premier League rival a permanent deal?

794. Can you name two of the three goalkeepers that the Hammers signed ahead of the 2012/13 campaign?

795. England international midfielder Matt Jarvis made his Premier League debut for the Hammers against which club?

796. At which Premier League ground did West Ham secure their first away win of the 2012/13 season?

797. Which midfielder scored more Premier League goals for the Hammers in 2012/13 - Mark Noble or Mo Diame?

798. Modibo Maiga made the most substitute appearances for West Ham in 2012/13 - in how many Premier League fixtures did he appear from the bench - 15, 16 or 17?

799. Who was the only West Ham player to hit double figures in the Premier League scoring charts in 2012/13?

800. How many Premier League fixtures did the Hammers win in 2012/13?

SCOTT PARKER

801. Who was the West Ham manager when Scott joined the club?

802. From which club did the Hammers sign Scott?

803. Can you name the two non-London clubs that Scott played for in his professional career?

804. Parker won three England caps while with West Ham - true or false?

805. Against which club did Parker make his Premier League debut for West Ham?

806. In which season was Scott voted Hammer of the Year for the final time?

807. Other than Parker, which other West Ham player has been presented with the Hammer of the Year award in three consecutive seasons?

808. How many Premier League goals did Parker score for West Ham - seven, eight or nine?

809. Other than West Ham can you name the five clubs that Scott has played Premier League football for?

810. With which club did Parker begin his managerial career?

GIANFRANCO ZOLA

811. West Ham United were the first club that Gianfranco Zola managed - true or false?

812. Which coaching role did Zola hold prior to joining the Hammers?

813. In which season was he appointed Hammers boss?

814. Who did he succeed in the Boleyn Ground hot-seat?

815. A full Italian international, how many goals did Zola score for this country - more than ten, less than ten or ten exactly?

816. What final Premier League position did Zola guide West Ham to in his first season at the helm?

817. Which youngster did Zola hand a Premier League debut to in the first home game of the 2009/10 season?

818. Who did the Hammers face in Zola's final game as boss?

819. Can you name the two English clubs that Zola managed following his spell with West Ham?

820. What position did Zola hold during the 2018/19 season?

THE 2013/14 SEASON

821. Which newly-promoted side did West Ham face in their opening Premier League fixture of 2013/14?

822. Can you name the manager who guided his club to the 2013/14 Premier League title?

823. Which three clubs were relegated from the Premier League in 2013/14?

824. On Boxing Day 2013 the Hammers suffered a 3-1 home defeat to which London rival?

825. Who scored West Ham's first Premier League goal in the calendar year of 2014?

826. Which player saw red in the New Year's Day match away to Fulham?

827. Can you name the Premier League side that the Hammers faced at the semi-final stage of the 2013/14 League Cup?

828. Who was the Hammers' captain in the 2013/14 season?

829. Which Romanian international joined West Ham ahead of the 2013/14 season?

830. On the eve of the new season, West Ham signed winger Stewart Downing from which club?

831. Can you name the two managers who have taken charge of West Ham in the Premier League and also managed Watford?

832. In which Premier League campaign did the Hammers first face Watford?

833. West Ham won their first Premier League match with Watford 1-0 - can you name the Hammers' goalscorer?

834. Where was the first Premier League match between the two clubs played - Vicarage Road, the Boleyn Ground or London Stadium?

835. Who netted a brace for the Hammers in a 3-1 win in Watford's last ever trip to the Boleyn Ground in April 2016?

836. Which West Ham striker opened the scoring in the 2-0 Premier League victory at home to the Hornets in 2017/18?

837. In which season did the Hammers face the Hornets in the Premier League and also the FA Cup?

838. Ahead of the 2019/20 season, the Hammers have only once recorded a Premier League double over Watford - true or false?

839. Midfielder Valon Behrami has played Premier League football for both clubs - which country does he represent internationally?

840. Can you name the goalkeeper who joined the Hammers on loan in 2011/12 and later played in the Premier League for Watford?

DAVID MOYES

841. With which club did Moyes first manage in the Premier League?

842. Moyes began his managerial career at Preston North End. He had previously played for Preston - true or false?

843. In which season did Moyes guide North End to the Second Division title - 1997/98, 1998/99 or 1999/2000?

844. Following his spell as manager of Manchester United, which other Premier League side did he manage before arriving at West Ham?

845. As manager of West Ham, Moyes lost more games than he won - true or false?

846. Which former Hammer and England international did Moyes name among his coaching staff at West Ham?

847. After just eleven months in charge of Manchester United, which Spanish club did Moyes manage before returning to the Premier League?

848. Moyes' reign at West Ham began with a 2-0 Premier League defeat away to which club?

849. Who were the opposition when Moyes won his first game as Hammers boss?

850. Why was the Hammers' Premier League victory over Huddersfield Town in January 2018 a landmark occasion for Moyes?

QUIZ 86
THE 2014/15 SEASON

851. The Hammers began the 2014/15 season with two London derby fixtures - who did they play in their opening two Premier League games?

852. Who knocked West Ham out of the League Cup on penalties in 2014/15?

853. What was the Hammers' longest winning sequence of Premier League games in 2014/15?

854. Ahead of the 2014/15 season, West Ham signed Aaron Cresswell from which Championship club?

855. Can you name the Ecuadorian forward who joined the Hammers from Mexican club Pachuca in the summer of 2014?

856. In which month was boss Sam Allardyce voted Manger of the Month?

857. Who ended the season as the Hammers' leading scorer in the Premier League?

858. Which summer signing ended his first season at the club by landing the Hammer of the Year award?

859. What was the Hammers' final league position in 2014/15?

860. Manager Sam Allardyce left the club at the end of the season, who were final club he faced as Hammers' boss?

QUIZ 87
ROBERT SNODGRASS

861. With which Scottish club did Snodgrass begin his professional career?

862. Who were the first English club that Robert played for?

863. Can you name the former West Ham player who was managing Norwich City when Snodgrass joined the Canaries?

864. In November 2013 Snodgrass opened the scoring for Norwich in the Hammers' 3-1 defeat at Carrow Road - true or false?

865. In which season did Snodgrass join the Hammers?

866. From which club did West Ham sign him?

867. Who was the Hammers' manager when Robert joined the club?

868. Snodgrass' first start for the Hammers coincided with a 3-1 Premier League away win to which club?

869. The 2017/18 season saw Snodgrass join which club on loan?

870. Against which club did Snodgrass score his first Premier League goal for the Hammers?

MANUEL PELLEGRINI

871. What nationality is West Ham boss Manuel Pellegrini?

872. In 2009/10, as manager of Real Madrid, Pellegrini saw his side amass 96 points and still not win the title - true or false?

873. In which season did Pellegrini first manage in the Premier League?

874. On how many occasions was he a League Cup winner with Manchester City?

875. Who scored the first Premier League goal in Pellegrini's reign as West Ham boss?

876. What is Pellegrini's title at London Stadium - first team manager or head coach?

877. On which ground did Manuel secure his first Premier League win as West Ham boss?

878. What final league position did Pellegrini lead the Hammers to in his first season with the club?

879. Who is Manuel's assistant at London Stadium?

880. As at the start of the 2019/20 season, Pellegrini is the oldest manager in the Premier League - true or false?

881. What was historic about the 2015/16 season for the Hammers?

882. Which Romanian club knocked the Hammers out of the Europa League in 2015/16?

883. Who scored West Ham's first Premier League goal of the season at the Boleyn Ground?

884. Can you recall which West Ham player was sent off in the opening home game of the Premier League campaign?

885. Which club won the Premier League title in 2015/16?

886. Which long-serving midfielder was handed a testimonial match during the 2015/16 season?

887. Who did the Hammers defeat in the final home game of the season?

888. Who ended the season as the team's leading scorer in the Premier League?

889. In which position did the Hammers end the 2015/16 season?

890. The 2015/16 season ended with the team amassing a club record 62 Premier League points - true or false?

2019/20 SQUAD NUMBERS

Without peeking at a Hammers programme can you give the following players their 2019/20 squad number?

891. Angelo Ogbonna?

892. Mark Noble?

893. Felipe Anderson?

894. Sebastien Haller?

895. Michail Antonio?

896. Ryan Fredericks?

897. Declan Rice?

898. Andriy Yarmolenko?

899. Winston Reid?

900. David Martin?

QUIZ 91
TOTTENHAM HOTSPUR

901. Tottenham Hotspur have provided opposition in every one of West Ham's Premier League campaigns - true or false?

902. On how many different venues have Premier League fixtures between the Hammers and Spurs been played?

903. Who has managed both clubs in Premier League fixtures?

904. Which three-time winner of the Hammer of the Year award left West Ham to join Spurs?

905. When Jermain Defoe joined Spurs in 2004, which striker moved in the opposite direction?

906. What trophy did Michael Carrick win with West Ham before joining Spurs in 2004?

907. Can you recall the reported transfer fee that West Ham received from Spurs for Michael Carrick?

908. Ahead of the 2019/20 season, when did the Hammers last complete a Premier League double over Spurs?

909. Who scored the only goal of the game to give the Hammers their first Premier League triumph over Spurs in February 1996?

910. Can you name the West Ham scorer from their 1-0 win over Spurs in September 2010?

THE 2016/17 SEASON

911. Which Italian giant did the Hammers welcome to the London Stadium for a pre-season Betway Cup game?

912. Domzale were the first team to visit London Stadium for a Europa League tie, what country were Domzale from?

913. Stoke City provided the opposition for the Hammers' first Premier League game of 2016/17 - true or false?

914. Who scored West Ham's first goal of their 2016/17 Premier League campaign?

915. Which Premier League opponent attracted the biggest crowd of the season to London Stadium?

916. Ahead of the 2016/17 season, from which club did West Ham sign Manuel Lanzini on a permanent basis?

917. Who were the first Premier League side to defeat West Ham at London Stadium?

918. In which league position did the Hammers end their 2016/17 campaign?

919. How many Premier League fixtures did the Hammers win at home in 2016/17 - seven, eight or nine?

920. Who ended the season as the club's leading scorer with nine goals?

QUIZ 93
WEST BROMWICH ALBION

921. Who has managed both West Ham and the Baggies in the Premier League?

922. Can you name the Scottish international midfielder who played in the Premier League for both clubs?

923. Former West Ham defender Danny Gabbidon began his professional career with West Bromwich Albion - true or false?

924. In which season did the two clubs first play one another in the Premier League?

925. Who scored both goals in the Hammers' 2-1 win at the Hawthorns in February 2003?

926. Can you name the West Ham 'keeper who kept two Premier League clean sheets against the Albion in 2005/06?

927. In which season did the Hammers stage a remarkable second-half comeback at the Hawthorns when they came from 3-0 down at the break to draw 3-3?

928. Can you name the Hammers' scorers from the above 3-3 draw?

929. Which West Ham striker netted both goals in the 2-1 win over West Brom at London Stadium in 2017/18?

930. Both of the Baggies' first two visits to the London Stadium have ended in defeats - true or false?

WIGAN ATHLETIC

931. Ahead of the 2019/20 season, in which Premier League campaign did the Hammers last face Wigan?

932. The Latics' last season in the Premier League saw the club relegated and win the FA Cup - true or false?

933. The Hammers last Premier League match with Wigan ended in a 2-0 home win for the Hammers - can you name the two scorers?

934. Who in the 2005/06 season scored the Hammers' first Premier League goal against Wigan?

935. Can you name the defender who help West Ham to Premier League promotion in 2005 and later managed Wigan?

936. Who turned from hero to villain in March 2009 when he opened the scoring away to Wigan before later being sent off?

937. Who, together with West Ham and Wigan, were promoted to the Premier League in 2005?

938. For how many consecutive seasons did Wigan compete in the Premier League - eight, nine or ten?

939. Who was the West Ham manager when they last played Wigan in the Premier League?

940. On how many occasions have Premier League fixtures between the Hammers and Latics ended 0-0 - never, once or twice?

941. Wimbledon never played Premier League football at Plough Lane - true or false?

942. At which London venue was the first Premier League match between the Hammers and the Dons played?

943. In which season did the Hammers and Dons first meet as Premier League rivals?

944. Who scored a brace for West Ham in their first Premier League victory over Wimbledon?

945. At which end of the Boleyn Ground did Paulo Di Canio score his 1999/2000 Goal of the Season against Wimbledon?

946. Who was the Dons goalkeeper on the receiving end of Di Canio's brilliance in 2000?

947. A game always remembered for Di Canio's wonderful volley, but who scored the Hammers' second goal in the 2-1 win over the Dons in March 2000?

948. In which season did the Hammers record their only Premier League double over the Dons?

949. John Hartson became the Dons' most expensive signing when he joined Wimbledon from West Ham in January 1999. What was the fee that the Hammers received for him?

950. Who netted the only goal of the game to give the Hammers a 1-0 win away to Wimbledon in October 1995 - Iain Dowie, Robbie Slater or Tony Cottee?

THE 2017/18 SEASON

951. Which event prevented the Hammers from playing a home game until September 2017?

952. Who did the Hammers finally face in their first home game of the season?

953. Which Hammer saw red in the second game of the season away to Southampton?

954. Who did the Hammers knock out of the League Cup at the second round stage?

955. On which away ground did West Ham secure their first away point of the season in 2017/18?

956. A 4-1 defeat at home to which Premier League side signalled the end of Slaven Bilic's reign as West Ham manager?

957. Who scored the first goal of David Moyes' tenure as West Ham boss?

958. In what position in the Premier League table were the Hammers when David Moyes took over as manager?

959. What was the Hammers final placing in the 2017/18 Premier League table?

960. Which Premier League rival knocked the Hammers out of the League Cup at the quarter-final stage?

QUIZ 97
WOLVERHAMPTON WANDERERS

961. Prior to the 2019/20 season, in how many Premier League campaigns have the Hammers faced Wolves - three, four or five?

962. In which season did the two clubs first meet in the Premier League?

963. Who scored West Ham's first Premier League goal against Wolves in a 2-0 win at Molineux?

964. Who was the first manager to take charge of the Hammers for a Premier League match against Wolves at London Stadium?

965. Which future West Ham player netted for Wolves in the 1-1 draw in October 2010?

966. An own goal gave West Ham the lead but who scored the second goal in the 2-0 win over Wolves at the Boleyn Ground on New Year's Day 2011?

967. Wolves visited the Boleyn Ground during the Hammers' farewell season to their former home - in which competition did they meet?

968. In March 2010 who scored the Hammers' late consolation goal in a 3-1 defeat at home to Wolves?

969. Who managed West Ham in their first ever Premier League match against Wolves?

970. Ahead of the 2019/20 season can you name the West Ham player who featured in both the first and most recent Premier League games between the two clubs?

Javier Hernandez netted West Ham's first Premier League goal of 2019/20 in a 1-1 draw at Brighton. Can you recall Hernandez's ten teammates who helped secure the first point in the Hammers' latest Premier League adventure? (4-5-1 formation with Hernandez up top)

971. Goalkeeper? (six letters & nine letters)

972. Right-back? (four letter & ten letters)

973. Central defender? (six letter & seven letters)

974. Central defender? (four letters & four letters)

975. Left-back? (six letters & seven letters)

976. Right midfield? (five letters & seven letters)

977. Central midfield? (six letters & four letters)

978. Central midfielder? (six letters & seven letters)

979. Central midfield? (four letters & eight letters)

980. Left midfield? (six letters & nine letters)

981. Against which club did the Hammers record their first Premier League win of 2018/19?

982. Ahead of the 2018/19 season, West Ham signed defender Issa Diop from which club?

983. Summer signing Lukasz Fabianski kept his first Premier League clean sheet against which club?

984. Striker Jordan Hugill joined which Championship side on loan for the 2018/19 campaign?

985. Which Premier League rival knocked the Hammers out of the League Cup?

986. In April 2019, West Ham became the first club to defeat Tottenham Hotspur in their new stadium - true or false?

987. Who ended the season as the club's leading Premier League scorer?

988. Which club did West Ham face in both the League Cup and the FA Cup in 2018/19?

989. How many Premier League goals did the Hammers score in 2018/19 - 52, 53 or 54?

990. Against which club did defender Issa Diop score his first Premier League goal?

QUIZ 100
FINAL DAY FIXTURES

991. Against which club will the Hammers complete their 2019/20 Premier League campaign?

992. Who scored twice as West Ham ended their 2018/19 season with an emphatic 4-1 win away to Watford?

993. Can you name the opposition who were already relegated from the Premier League when they travelled to the Boleyn Ground on the final day of the 2012/13 season?

994. Which Hammer netted a final day hat-trick in the 2012/13 season?

995. Who scored the Hammers' final goal of 1994/95 when they drew 1-1 at home to Manchester United?

996. Which ground hosted the final game of the Hammers' 2015/16 Premier League campaign?

997. Carlos Tevez netted the goal that secured the Hammers' Premier League status with a 1-0 win at Old Trafford on the final day of 2006/07 - which goalkeeper did he score past?

998. Who was the West Ham 'keeper that kept a clean sheet against Manchester United in the vital 2006/07 win at Old Trafford?

999. Who were the visitors to the Boleyn Ground for a final day goalless stalemate in 1999/2000?

1000. Who scored the opening goal of the game in the Hammers' thrilling 4-3 final day victory over Leicester City in 1997/98?

ANSWERS

QUIZ 1 · THE PREMIER LEAGUE

1. 1992/93
2. 20
3. Six (Manchester United, Blackburn Rovers, Arsenal, Chelsea, Manchester City and Leicester City)
4. 1993/94
5. 2019/20 will have been the Hammers 24th Premier League campaign
6. Barclays
7. The Hammers have played 48 different clubs at Premier League level
8. 13 (eleven permanent plus Brooking and Keen as caretakers)
9. Mark Noble
10. Two (Cardiff City and Swansea City)

QUIZ 2 · THE 1993/94 SEASON

11. Billy Bonds
12. Wimbledon
13. The Boleyn Ground
14. Dale Gordon (away to Coventry City)
15. Sheffield Wednesday
16. Ewood Park (Blackburn Rovers)
17. Trevor Morley
18. Manchester United
19. Southampton
20. 13th

QUIZ 3 · ARSENAL

21. Ludek Miklosko
22. Martin Allen
23. True
24. 1997/98
25. 2006/07
26. Arsenal 2 West Ham United 3
27. John Hartson
28. Andy Carroll
29. 2018/19
30. False

QUIZ 4 · ASTON VILLA

31. True
32. Tony Cottee (September 1994)
33. 2005/06
34. Marlon Harewood
35. Cheikhou Kouyate
36. Aston Villa 1 West Ham United 1

37. John Hartson
38. False (Sam Allardyce has never managed Aston Villa)
39. Dean Ashton
40. James Collins

QUIZ 5 · BARNSLEY

41. 1997/98
42. True
43. Oakwell
44. Harry Redknapp
45. Neil Redfearn
46. Frank Lampard (Jnr) and John Hartson
47. Five
48. Samassi Abou
49. Craig Forrest
50. True

QUIZ 6 · BIRMINGHAM CITY

51. 2002/03
52. Joe Cole
53. Trevor Brooking
54. Marlon Harewood
55. 2005/06
56. Mark Noble
57. Lee Bowyer
58. True
59. League Cup (semi-final)
60. 2010/11

QUIZ 7 · CAPTAIN CALLING

61. Ludek Miklosko

62. Tim Breaker
63. David Burrows
64. Tony Gale
65. Martin Allen
66. Ian Bishop
67. Mike Marsh
68. Matthew Rush
69. Danny Williamson
70. Trevor Morley

QUIZ 8 · THE 1994/95 SEASON

71. Ludek Miklosko and Steve Potts
72. Six
73. Aston Villa
74. Don Hutchison
75. Tony Cottee
76. Ipswich Town
77. Tony Cottee (13 Premier League goals)
78. Michael Hughes
79. Steve Potts
80. 14th

QUIZ 9 · BLACKBURN ROVERS

81. Blackburn 4 West Ham United 2 and West Ham United 2 Blackburn 0
82. 1993/94
83. True
84. Sam Allardyce
85. Shaka Hislop

86. 2006/07
87. Dean Ashton
88. Freddie Sears
89. Lucas Neill
90. Thomas Hitzlsperger

QUIZ 10 · BLACKPOOL

91. 2010/11
92. Ian Holloway
93. Avram Grant
94. The Boleyn Ground
95. Robert Green (West Ham) and Matt Gilks (Blackpool)
96. Marlon Harewood
97. Victor Obinna
98. Robbie Keane
99. Birmingham City
100. True

QUIZ 11 · HAMMER OF THE YEAR

101. Trevor Morley (1993/94)
102. Julian Dicks (1995/96 and 1996/97)
103. Shaka Hislop (1998/99)
104. Sebastien Schemmel
105. Joe Cole
106. Seven
107. Stuart Pearce
108. Robert Green
109. 2008/09
110. Rio Ferdinand

QUIZ 12 · HARRY REDKNAPP

111. 1994/95
112. Michael Carrick
113. Queens Park Rangers
114. Iain Dowie and Keith Rowland
115. Florin Raducioiu
116. Fifth
117. 1998/99
118. Frank Lampard (Snr)
119. Southampton
120. Glenn Roeder

QUIZ 13 · BOLTON WANDERERS

121. False
122. The League Cup
123. Ian Pearce
124. 1995/96
125. True
126. Harry Redknapp
127. John Hartson
128. Ian Bishop (1995/96)
129. Newcastle United
130. Five (two Premier League games, two FA Cup ties and one League Cup tie)

QUIZ 14 · BOURNEMOUTH

131. False (they met in the old Second Division in 1989/90)
132. Jermain Defoe

133. Slaven Bilic
134. Callum Wilson
135. Mark Noble
136. False
137. Dimitri Payet
138. West Ham United 1 Bournemouth 0
139. James Collins
140. True

QUIZ 15 · BRADFORD CITY

141. True
142. Paulo Di Canio
143. True
144. Eight
145. Joe Cole
146. Dan Petrescu
147. Frank Lampard (Jnr)
148. Billy McKinlay
149. Paul Jewell
150. 2000/01

QUIZ 16 · THE 1995/96 SEASON

151. Danny Williamson
152. Marco Boogers
153. Seven (v Everton)
154. Wimbledon
155. Liverpool
156. False
157. Tony Cottee and Julian Dicks
158. Coventry City

159. Kenny Brown (Jnr)
160. Rio Ferdinand

QUIZ 17 · CAPTAIN CALLING

161. Shaka Hislop
162. Ian Pearce
163. Rio Ferdinand
164. Neil Ruddock
165. Andy Impey
166. Frank Lampard
167. Eyal Berkovic
168. Stan Lazaridis
169. Trevor Sinclair
170. Ian Wright

QUIZ 18 · BRIGHTON & HOVE ALBION

171. Chris Hughton
172. 2017/18
173. Javier Hernandez
174. Slaven Bilic
175. True
176. Marko Arnautovic
177. False
178. Championship
179. True
180. The Amex

QUIZ 19 · OPENING DAY FIXTURES

181. Ian Wright
182. Tottenham Hotspur
183. Teddy Sheringham
184. Charlton Athletic

185. Bobby Zamora
186. Aston Villa
187. Cheikhou Kouyate
188. Reece Oxford
189. Craig Bellamy
    (Cardiff City)
190. Liverpool

QUIZ 20 · BURNLEY

191. Gianfranco Zola
192. Carlton Cole
    and Luis Jimenez
193. Ilan
194. 2014/15
195. Joe Hart
196. Mark Noble
197. Ghanaian
198. Felipe Anderson
199. 2017/18
200. Darren Randolph

QUIZ 21 · CARDIFF CITY

201. 2013/14
202. Malky Mackay
203. Howard Webb
204. Joe Cole
205. True
206. Jussi Jaaskelainen
207. James Tomkins
208. True
209. Lucas Perez
210. Fulham and
    Huddersfield Town

QUIZ 22 · CHARLTON ATHLETIC

211. Alan Curbishley
    and Alan Pardew
212. Paul Kitson
213. True
214. Chelsea, Newcastle
    United, Tottenham
    Hotspur and Fulham
215. 1998/99
216. 2006/07
217. Three
218. Paulo Di Canio
219. David James
220. Richard Rufus

QUIZ 23 · CHELSEA

221. True
222. £11M
223. Trevor Morley
224. Demba Ba
225. 1999/2000
226. Gianfranco Zola
227. 2002/03
228. Yossi Benayon
229. Sixth minute
230. Glen Johnson

QUIZ 24 · COVENTRY CITY

231. Craig Bellamy
    and John Hartson
232. True
233. Highfield Road
234. Iain Dowie

235. Shaka Hislop
236. Michael Carrick
237. West Ham United
238. Tony Cottee & Mark Reiper
239. Joe Cole
240. Christian Dailly

QUIZ 25 · THE 1996/97 SEASON

241. Paulo Futre
242. Eight
243. Teddy Sheringham
244. Julian Dicks
245. West Ham United 4
Tottenham Hotspur 3
246. Marc Reiper
247. Czech
248. Les Sealey
and Steve Mautone
249. Aston Villa
250. Slaven Bilic

QUIZ 26 · BOXING DAY FIXTURES

251. Marko Arnautovic
252. Tony Cottee
253. Swansea City
254. Carlton Cole
255. Birmingham City
256. False (they had drawn 1-1 earlier in the season)
257. Portsmouth
258. Nolberto Solano
259. Craig Bellamy
260. Robert Green

QUIZ 27 · CRYSTAL PALACE

261. Don Hutchison
262. False
263. 2016/17
264. 2014/15
265. Mark Noble
266. Manuel Lanzini
267. Aaron Cresswell
268. James Tomkins
269. True
270. Danny Gabbidon

QUIZ 28 · DERBY COUNTY

271. Paulo Wanchope
272. Stephen Bywater
273. Eleven
274. 1996/97
275. West Ham United 1
Derby County 1
276. Ian Bishop
277. True
278. West Ham United 5
Derby County 1
and Derby County 0
West Ham United 2
279. Tyrone Mears
280. Frank Lampard (Jnr)

QUIZ 29 · EVERTON

281. True
282. Andriy Yarmolenko
283. Tim Breacker
284. Manuel Lanzini
285. Kevin Campbell

286. Sam Allardyce and David Moyes
287. True
288. Manuel Pellegrini
289. Croatian
290. West Ham (24 Premier League games for the Hammers v 5 for Everton)

QUIZ 30 · THE 1997/98 SEASON

291. Eighth place
292. Newcastle United and Southampton
293. Barnsley and Wimbledon
294. John Harston
295. Hartson scored 15 Premier League goals
296. Trevor Sinclair and Eyal Berkovic
297. Bernard Lama
298. More than 55 (they scored 56)
299. Arsenal
300. Crystal Palace

QUIZ 31 · FULHAM

301. West Ham won 1-0
302. Scott Parker
303. 2001/02
304. Frederic Kanoute
305. Michail Antonio
306. True
307. 53 seconds
308. Bobby Zamora
309. Tony Warner
310. False (the Hammers' first double over Fulham was in 2005/06)

QUIZ 32 · HUDDERSFIELD TOWN

311. False (they played in the old First Division in 1970/71)
312. Slaven Bilic
313. True
314. Pedro Obiang
315. Huddersfield Town 1 West Ham United 4
316. False (they played a League Cup tie there in 1997, when it was known as the McAlpine Stadium)
317. Felipe Anderson
318. Javier Hernandez
319. Mark Noble
320. Joe Hart

QUIZ 33 · HULL CITY

321. 2016/17
322. 2008/09
323. True
324. Two
325. Robert Snodgrass
326. True
327. Five times
328. Mark Noble
329. West Ham 3 Hull City 0

330. Mohamed Diame

QUIZ 34 · IPSWICH TOWN

331. Lee Chapman
332. False (Ipswich won 1-0 in 2000/01)
333. £3.75M
334. True
335. John Lyall
336. Claus Thomsen
337. Matt Holland
338. Jermain Defoe
339. Matthew Rush
340. Ipswich Town 1 West Ham United 2

QUIZ 35 · THE 1998/99 SEASON

341. Manchester United, Arsenal, Chelsea and Leeds United
342. Frank Lampard (Jnr)
343. Nine
344. Marc-Vivien Foe
345. Wimbledon
346. Shaka Hislop
347. Benfica
348. The Intertoto Cup
349. True
350. Five

QUIZ 36 · SAM ALLARDYCE

351. True
352. Blackburn Rovers
353. 2011

354. True
355. Tenth (in 2012/13)
356. Four
357. Aston Villa
358. Twelfth (in 2014/15)
359. Newcastle United
360. Sunderland

QUIZ 37 · JACK WILSHERE

361. Arsenal
362. Bolton Wanderers
363. 2016/17
364. Manuel Pellegrini
365. He agreed a three-year contract
366. Liverpool
367. Number 19
368. Eight
369. Newcastle United
370. 34

QUIZ 38 · LEEDS UNITED

371. 2002/03
372. Rio Ferdinand
373. False (they failed to score in their first three meetings)
374. Jeroen Boere
375. John Hartson
376. Ian Wright, Shaka Hislop and Steve Lomas
377. Rob Harris
378. Nigel Winterburn
379. False

380. Seven
(West Ham United 3
Leeds United 4
in November 2002)

QUIZ 39 · LEICESTER CITY

381. Brian Deane
382. West Ham United 1
Leicester City 2
and Leicester City 2
West Ham United 2
383. 1994/95
384. Mark Noble
385. Three times (1994/95,
1996/97 and 1999/2000)
386. The Boleyn Ground
387. True
388. Julian Dicks
389. Ghanaian
390. Frank Lampard (Jnr)

QUIZ 40 · LIVERPOOL

391. Michail Antonio
392. Andy Carroll
393. Darren Randolph
394. Mark Noble
395. 1994/95
396. Don Hutchison
397. Paul Ince
398. Slaven Bilic (2015/16)
399. Chelsea, Portsmouth
and Stoke City
400. Arsenal, Chelsea, Everton,
Manchester United
and Tottenham Hotspur

QUIZ 41 · MANCHESTER CITY

401. Pablo Fornals
402. West Ham United 2
Manchester City 2
403. Enner Valencia
404. 2015/16
405. Diafra Sakho
406. Craig Bellamy
407. Manuel Pellegrini
408. Boleyn Ground, London
Stadium, Maine Road
and Etihad Stadium
409. 1993/94
410. False

QUIZ 42 · THE 1999/2000 SEASON

411. 62 days
412. Jokerit (Finland)
413. UEFA Cup
414. Frank Lampard (Jnr)
415. Bradford City
416. Trevor Sinclair
417. 52 goals
418. 55 points
419. Paulo Di Canio (16
Premier League goals)
420. True (they finished ninth)

QUIZ 43 · MANCHESTER UNITED

421. Manchester United
422. True
423. Carlos Tevez
424. Winston Reid

425. 2006/07
426. Jermain Defoe
427. Robert Green
428. West Ham United 0 Manchester United 2
429. Victor Lindelof
430. The dropping of two points cost Manchester Utd the Premier League title

QUIZ 44 · MIDDLESBROUGH

431. Iain Dowie
432. False (all Boro/West Ham Premier League games have been at the Riverside)
433. West Ham United
434. 2007/08
435. Andy Carroll
436. Darren Randolph
437. Gary O'Neill
438. Tony Cottee
439. Dimitri Payet
440. False (Boro were relegated in '96/97, West Ham were 14th)

QUIZ 45 · SEBASTIEN HALLER

441. Eintracht Frankfurt
442. £45M
443. True
444. French
445. Auxerre
446. FC Utrecht
447. 13
448. 15
449. Hertha Berlin
450. Manchester City

QUIZ 46 · NEWCASTLE UNITED

451. True
452. Coventry City, Blackburn Rovers, Liverpool, Manchester City and Cardiff City
453. Liverpool
454. £7M
455. 1992/93
456. Billy Bonds
457. Tim Breacker
458. Robert Lee
459. 1998/99
460. Declan Rice

QUIZ 47 · NORWICH CITY

461. Sam Byram
462. Robert Snodgrass
463. True
464. Robert Green
465. 1993/94
466. True
467. Twice
468. Cheikhou Kouyate
469. Chris Hughton
470. True

QUIZ 48 · THE 2000/01 SEASON

471. Seven

472. Coventry City (away)
473. 15th
474. Bradford City, Coventry City and Manchester City
475. October
476. Newcastle United
477. Paulo Di Canio
478. Frederic Kanoute
479. Harry Redknapp
480. Glenn Roeder

QUIZ 49 · BOBBY DAZZLER

481. Jimmy Walker
482. Tomas Repka
483. Chris Powell
484. Elliott Ward
485. Anton Ferdinand
486. Nigel Reo-Coker
487. Shaun Newton
488. Hayden Mullins
489. Marlon Harewood
490. Matthew Etherington

QUIZ 50 · NOTTINGHAM FOREST

491. Four
492. 1998/99
493. West Ham United 2 Nottingham Forest 1 (February 1999)
494. Mark Bowen
495. Marc Rieper
496. Marlon Harewood
497. Stuart Pearce

498. False
499. Julian Dicks
500. True

QUIZ 51 · OLDHAM ATHLETIC

501. True
502. Two
503. 1993/94
504. Trevor Morley
505. Alvin Martin
506. Ludek Miklosko
507. Billy Bonds
508. Joe Royle
509. True
510. Five

QUIZ 52 · PORTSMOUTH

511. David James
512. Harry Redknapp
513. 2009/10
514. Matthew Upson
515. True
516. Portsmouth 1 West Ham United 1
517. James Collins
518. Gary O'Neil
519. Hayden Mullins
520. 2006/07

QUIZ 53 · CAPTAIN CALLING

521. Darren Randolph
522. Winston Reid
523. Angelo Ogbonna
524. Aaron Cresswell

525. Cheikhou Kouyate
526. Manuel Lanzini
527. Michail Antonio
528. Andy Carroll
529. Diafra Sakho
530. Dimitri Payet

QUIZ 54 · THE 2001/02 SEASON

531. Glenn Roeder
532. Christian Dailly
533. David James and Shaka Hislop
534. Seventh
535. Dr Martens
536. Fila
537. Sebastien Schemmel
538. Charlton Athletic
539. Derby County
540. Bolton Wanderers

QUIZ 55 · QUEENS PARK RANGERS

541. Bobby Zamora
542. Andy Impey
543. Manchester City
544. Harry Redknapp
545. False
546. 2014/15
547. Adrian
548. Tony Cottee
549. Matt Jarvis
550. True

QUIZ 56 · READING

551. 2003/04
552. Reece Oxford
553. Shaka Hislop
554. Three
555. Kevin Nolan
556. West Ham United 4 Reading 2
557. 2006/07
558. Matthew Etherington
559. Nolberto Solano
560. Steve Clarke

QUIZ 57 · SHEFFIELD UNITED

561. False (Norwich City were the first promoted club the Hammers faced)
562. League Cup (2014/15)
563. Ravel Morrison
564. 2006/07
565. 1993/94
566. Hayden Mullins
567. Robert Green
568. 0-0
569. Dave Bassett
570. Don Hutchison

QUIZ 58 · THE 2002/03 SEASON

571. Ten seasons
572. West Bromwich Albion and Sunderland
573. Trevor Brooking

574. 42
575. True
576. Paulo Di Canio
577. £3
578. January 2003
(v Blackburn Rovers)
579. Chelsea
580. St Andrew's
(Birmingham City)

QUIZ 59 · SHEFFIELD WEDNESDAY

581. Paulo Di Canio
582. Michail Antonio
583. Chris Woods
584. Clive Allen
585. Paul Kitson
586. John Hartson
587. 4-3
588. 1999/2000
589. Seven
590. Iain Dowie

QUIZ 60 · SOUTHAMPTON

591. Felipe Anderson
592. Ryan Fredericks
593. False (only Harry Redknapp
managed both clubs
in the Premier League)
594. 1993/94
595. Trevor Morley
596. The Dell
597. Andy Carroll
598. 2000/01

599. Iain Dowie
600. St Mary's Stadium

QUIZ 61 · THE 2005/06 SEASON

601. Preston North End
602. 3-1
603. Alan Pardew
604. Bolton Wanderers
605. Dean Ashton
606. Jobserve
607. Ninth
608. True
609. Marlon Harewood
610. 14

QUIZ 62 · STOKE CITY

611. Matthew Etherington
612. Matthew Upson
613. Chelsea
614. True
615. £20M
616. 2010/11
617. 2008/09
618. True
619. Jack Collison
620. Andy Carroll

QUIZ 63 · SUNDERLAND

621. False (West Ham were
only relegated with
Sunderland once)
622. Roker Park
623. Sam Allardyce
and David Moyes

624. 1996/97
625. 0-0
626. Slaven Bilic
627. £5M
628. Winston Reid
629. 2000/01
630. Jermain Defoe

QUIZ 64 · THE 2006/07 SEASON

631. Watford
632. Palermo
633. Liverpool
634. Eggert Magnusson
635. Alan Pardew
636. Alan Curbishley
637. Eleven goals
638. 15th
639. Watford, Charlton Athletic and Sheffield United
640. Carlos Tevez

QUIZ 65 · AVRAM GRANT

641. Israeli
642. Gianfranco Zola
643. 2010/11
644. Thomas Hitzlsperger
645. Stoke City
646. Tottenham Hotspur
647. Portsmouth
648. Chelsea
649. Wigan Athletic
650. Sam Allardyce

QUIZ 66 · SWANSEA CITY

651. Swansea City
652. 1982/83
653. West Ham United 1 Swansea City 0
654. Lukasz Fabianski
655. Diafra Sakho
656. Michail Antonio
657. Andre Ayew
658. Swansea City 1 West Ham United 4
659. Slaven Bilic
660. 2016/17

QUIZ 67 · ALAN CURBISHLEY

661. Forest Gate
662. Under 100 (he made 85 league appearances for the Hammers)
663. Charlton Athletic
664. True
665. 2006/07
666. Manchester United
667. Nigel Reo-Coker
668. False
669. Harry Redknapp
670. Gianfranco Zola

QUIZ 68 · THE 2007/08 SEASON

671. Alan Curbishley
672. Ten
673. Four (Arsenal, Chelsea, Fulham and Tottenham)

674. 49 points
675. Tenth
676. Robert Green
& George McCartney
677. Third round (replay)
678. Everton
679. Christian Dailly
680. Aston Villa

QUIZ 69 · BILLY BONDS

681. Charlton Athletic
682. John Lyall
683. Lou Macari
684. True
685. 13th
686. Ludek Miklosko
687. Julian Dicks
688. Southampton
689. Harry Redknapp
690. Millwall

QUIZ 70 · SWINDON TOWN

691. True
692. 1993/94
693. The Boleyn Ground
694. West Ham United 0
Swindon Town 0
695. John Gorman
696. Billy Bonds
697. Trevor Morley
698. Jan-Aage Fjortoft
699. True
700. Frank McAvennie

QUIZ 71 · THE 2008/09 SEASON

701. Wigan Athletic
702. Dean Ashton
703. Craven Cottage (Fulham)
704. Paul Konchesky
705. Chelsea
706. September
707. Arsenal
708. Umbro
709. Robert Green
710. True (they finished ninth)

QUIZ 72 · JOE COLE

711. 1981
712. Paddington
713. 1998/99
714. Manchester United
715. Trevor Sinclair
716. West Ham United 5
Bradford City 4
717. True
718. Chelsea
719. Chelsea, Liverpool
and Aston Villa
720. Queens Park Rangers

QUIZ 73 · ALAN PARDEW

721. Crystal Palace
722. Charlton Athletic
723. 1989/90
724. 2003/04
725. False (he secured promotion
in his second season)

726. Ninth
727. Dean Ashton
728. Bolton Wanderers
729. Alan Curbishley
730. Charlton Athletic, Newcastle United, Crystal Palace and West Bromwich Albion

QUIZ 74 · THE 2009/10 SEASON

731. Wolverhampton Wanderers
732. One (Wolverhampton Wanderers)
733. Mark Noble
734. Robert Green
735. False
736. Carlton Cole
737. Burnley, Hull City and Portsmouth
738. 35 points
739. Burnley
740. Gianfranco Zola

QUIZ 75 · GLENN ROEDER

741. Leyton Orient
742. No
743. Queens Park Rangers
744. Gillingham
745. Glenn Hoddle
746. Harry Redknapp
747. 1999
748. Seventh

749. Newcastle United
750. Norwich City

QUIZ 76 · DECLAN RICE

751. 1999
752. Kingston upon Thames
753. Chelsea
754. 2016/17
755. Burnley
756. Southampton
757. Arsenal
758. Michael Carrick
759. Marko Arnautovic
760. Czech Republic

QUIZ 77 · THE 2010/11 SEASON

761. Blackpool and Birmingham City
762. Demba Ba
763. Seven goals
764. Semi-final
765. Birmingham City
766. Scott Parker
767. Ruud Boffin
768. Glen Johnson
769. £3.50
770. Sam Allardyce

QUIZ 78 · SLAVEN BILIC

771. Everton
772. Karlsruher SC
773. True
774. £1.3M
775. Harry Redknapp

776. Two goals
777. Croatia
778. 2015/16
779. Arsenal
780. Seventh

QUIZ 79 · PABLO ZABALETA

781. Twice (2011/12 and 2013/14)
782. False (He was signed by Mark Hughes)
783. Over 50
784. Number five
785. 2017/18
786. Slaven Bilic
787. Manchester United
788. 37
789. Espanyol
790. San Lorenzo

QUIZ 80 · THE 2012/13 SEASON

791. One season (2011/12)
792. Ravel Morrison
793. Sunderland
794. Stephen Henderson, Jussi Jaaskelainan and Raphael Spiegel
795. Swansea City
796. Loftus Road (Queens Park Rangers 1 West Ham United 2)
797. Mark Noble (Noble scored four goals to Diame's three)

798. 15
799. Kevin Nolan
800. Twelve

QUIZ 81 · SCOTT PARKER

801. Alan Curbishley
802. Newcastle United
803. Norwich City (loan) and Newcastle United
804. True
805. Arsenal
806. 2010/11
807. Trevor Brooking
808. Nine
809. Charlton Athletic, Chelsea, Newcastle United, Tottenham Hotspur and Fulham
810. Fulham

QUIZ 82 · GIANFRANCO ZOLA

811. True
812. Assistant manager to the Italian Under-21 side
813. 2008/09
814. Alan Curbishley
815. Ten exactly
816. Ninth
817. Zavon Hines
818. Manchester City
819. Watford and Birmingham City
820. Assistant manager at Chelsea

QUIZ 83 · THE 2013/14 SEASON

821. Cardiff City
822. Manuel Pellegrini (Manchester City)
823. Norwich City, Fulham and Cardiff City
824. Arsenal
825. Mo Diame
826. Kevin Nolan
827. Manchester City
828. Kevin Nolan
829. Razvan Rat
830. Liverpool

QUIZ 84 · WATFORD

831. Glenn Roeder and Gianfranco Zola
832. 1999/2000
833. Paulo Di Canio
834. Boleyn Ground
835. Mark Noble
836. Javier Hernandez
837. 2006/07
838. True (in 1999/2000)
839. Switzerland
840. Manuel Almunia

QUIZ 85 · DAVID MOYES

841. Everton
842. True
843. 1999/2000
844. Sunderland
845. True

846. Stuart Pearce
847. Real Sociedad
848. Watford
849. Chelsea
850. It was his 200th Premier League win as a manager

QUIZ 86 · THE 2014/15 SEASON

851. Tottenham Hotspur and Crystal Palace
852. Sheffield United
853. Three matches was the longest winning run (they managed this twice)
854. Ipswich Town
855. Enner Valencia
856. October 2014
857. Diafra Sakho
858. Aaron Cresswell
859. Twelfth
860. Newcastle United

QUIZ 87 · ROBERT SNODGRASS

861. Livingston
862. Leeds United
863. Chris Hughton
864. False (he scored the second goal)
865. 2016/17
866. Hull City
867. Slaven Bilic
868. Southampton

869. Aston Villa
870. Crystal Palace

QUIZ 88 · MANUEL PELLEGRINI

871. Chilean
872. True
873. 2013/14
874. Twice
875. Marko Arnautovic
876. First team manager
877. Goodison Park (Everton)
878. Tenth
879. Ruben Cousillas
880. False (Roy Hodgson was the oldest Premier League manager at the start of 2019/20)

QUIZ 89 · THE 2015/16 SEASON

881. It was the club's final season at the Boleyn Ground
882. Astra Giurgiu
883. Dimitri Payet
884. Adrian
885. Leicester City
886. Mark Noble
887. Manchester United
888. Andy Carroll
889. Seventh
890. True

QUIZ 90 · 2019/20 SQUAD NUMBERS

891. Angelo Ogbonna 21
892. Mark Noble 16
893. Felipe Anderson 8
894. Sebastien Haller 22
895. Michail Antonio 30
896. Ryan Fredericks 24
897. Declan Rice 41
898. Andriy Yarmolenko 7
899. Winston Reid 2
900. David Martin 25

QUIZ 91 · TOTTENHAM HOTSPUR

901. True
902. Five (Boleyn Ground, London Stadium, White Hart Lane, Wembley and Tottenham Hotspur Stadium)
903. Harry Redknapp
904. Scott Parker
905. Bobby Zamora
906. FA Youth Cup
907. £3.5M
908. 2013/14
909. Dani
910. Frederic Piquionne

QUIZ 92 · THE 2016/17 SEASON

911. Juventus
912. Slovenia

913. False (Chelsea were the first Premier League opponents in 2016/17)
914. James Collins
915. Manchester United (56,996)
916. Al-Jazira
917. Watford
918. Eleventh
919. Seven
920. Michail Antonio

QUIZ 93 · WEST BROMWICH ALBION

921. Alan Pardew
922. Nigel Quashie
923. True
924. 2002/03
925. Trevor Sinclair
926. Shaka Hislop
927. 2010/11
928. Demba Ba (2) and Carlton Cole
929. Andy Carroll
930. False (one game ended in a draw)

QUIZ 94 · WIGAN ATHLETIC

931. 2012/13
932. True
933. Matt Jarvis and Kevin Nolan
934. Marlon Harewood
935. Malky Mackay

936. Carlton Cole
937. Sunderland
938. Eight
939. Sam Allardyce
940. Never

QUIZ 95 · WIMBLEDON

941. True
942. The Boleyn Ground
943. 1993/94
944. Lee Chapman
945. The Centenary Stand end (later the Sir Trevor Brooking Stand and to those of a certain vintage the North Bank)
946. Neil Sullivan
947. Frederic Kanoute
948. 1997/98
949. £7.5M
950. Tony Cottee

QUIZ 96 · THE 2017/18 SEASON

951. The 2017 World Athletic Championships
952. Huddersfield Town
953. Marko Arnautovic
954. Cheltenham Town
955. The Hawthorns (a 0-0 draw with WBA)
956. Liverpool
957. Chiekhou Kouyate (v Leicester City)

958. 18th
959. 13th
960. Arsenal

QUIZ 97 · WOLVERHAMPTON WANDERERS

961. Three
962. 2009/10
963. Mark Noble
964. Manuel Pellegrini
965. Matt Jarvis
966. Freddie Sears
967. FA Cup
968. Guillermo Franco
969. Gianfranco Zola
970. Mark Noble

QUIZ 98 · OFF THE MARK FOR 2019/20

971. Lukasz Fabianski
972. Ryan Fredericks
973. Angelo Ogbonna
974. Issa Diop
975. Arthur Masuaku
976. Pablo Fornals
977. Declan Rice
978. Manuel Lanzini
979. Jack Wilshere
980. Robert Snodgrass

QUIZ 99 · THE 2018/19 SEASON

981. Everton
982. Toulouse

983. Wolverhampton Wanderers
984. Middlesbrough
985. Tottenham Hotspur
986. True
987. Marko Arnautovic
988. AFC Wimbledon
989. 52
990. Fulham

QUIZ 100 · FINAL DAY FIXTURES

991. Aston Villa
992. Mark Noble
993. Reading
994. Kevin Nolan
995. Michael Hughes
996. The Britannia Stadium (Stoke City)
997. Edwin van der Sar
998. Robert Green
999. Leeds United
1000. Frank Lampard (Jnr)